GCSE AQA

Combined Science
Biology
Foundation Level

There's a lot of Biology to learn in GCSE Combined Science... but this fantastic CGP book explains the facts, theory and practical skills with the clearest study notes around!

On top of all that, we've got exam-style questions in every topic — plus a set of Biology practice exam papers to *really* test you on what you've learned.

How to access your free Online Edition

This book includes a free Online Edition to read on your PC, Mac or tablet. You'll just need to go to **cgpbooks.co.uk/extras** and enter this code:

0652 2867 4452 0141

By the way, this code only works for one person. If somebody else has used this book before you, they might have already claimed the Online Edition.

Complete
Revision & Practice
Everything you need to pass the exams!

Contents

Throughout this book you'll see grade stamps like these: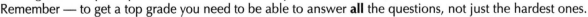

These grade stamps help to show how difficult the questions are.

Remember — to get a top grade you need to be able to answer **all** the questions, not just the hardest ones.

In the real exams, some questions test how well you can structure an answer (as well as your scientific knowledge). In this book, we've marked these questions with an asterisk (*).

Topic 4 — Bioenergetics

Topic 5 — Homeostasis and Response

Topic 6 — Inheritance, Variation and Evolution

Topic 7 — Ecology

Practical Skills

Practice Exams

Published by CGP

Editors: Luke Bennett, Ellen Burton, Katherine Faudemer and Emily Sheraton.

Contributor: Paddy Gannon.

From original material by Richard Parsons.

ISBN: 978 1 78908 002 5

With thanks to Karen Wells and Susan Alexander for the proofreading.

With thanks to Emily Smith for the copyright research.

With thanks to SPL for the image on page 180.

Printed by Elanders Ltd, Newcastle upon Tyne.

Clipart from Corel®

What to Expect in the Exams

It's nearly time to get cracking with your revision and exam practice. First, here's a handy guide to what you'll have to face in the exams and the special features of this book that we've included especially to help you. You're welcome.

1. Topics are Covered in Different Papers

For AQA Triology GCSE Combined Science, you'll sit six exam papers at the end of your course, including two biology exams.

You're expected to know the basic concepts of biology in both biology papers.

Paper	Time	No. of marks	Topics Assessed
Biology 1	1 hr 15 mins	70	1, 2, 3 and 4
Biology 2	1 hr 15 mins	70	5, 6 and 7

2. There are Different Question Types

In each exam, you'll be expected to answer a mixture of multiple choice questions, structured questions, questions that have short, closed answers, and open response questions.

For some open response questions, you'll be marked on the overall quality of your answer, not just its scientific content. So...

Fortunately, we've included loads of questions in this book, as well as a set of practice papers to give you the best possible preparation for the exams.

Always make sure:
- You answer the question fully.
- You include detailed, relevant information.
- Your answer is clear and has a logical structure.

In the exam practice questions, we've marked these questions with an asterisk (*).

3. You'll be Tested on Your Maths...

At least 20% of the total marks for GCSE Combined Science will come from questions that test your maths skills. For these questions, always remember to:

EXAMPLE:
Look out for these worked examples in this book — they show you maths skills you'll need in the exam.

- Show your working — you could get marks for this, even if your final answer's wrong.
- Check that the units of your answer are the same as the ones they asked for in the question.
- Make sure your answer is given to an appropriate number of significant figures.

4. ...and on Your Practical Skills

Whenever one of the required practicals crops up in this book, it's marked up with stamps like these...

...and there's a whole section on Practical Skills on pages 164-172.

- GCSE Combined Science contains 21 required practicals that you'll do during the course. The 7 biology practicals are covered in this book. You could be asked about these, and the practical skills involved in them, in the exams.
- At least 15% of the total marks will be for questions that test your understanding of the practical activities and practical skills.
- For example, you might be asked to comment on the design of an experiment (the apparatus and method), make predictions, analyse or interpret results... Pretty much anything to do with planning and carrying out the investigations.

5. You'll need to know about Working Scientifically

Working Scientifically is all about how real scientists use science in the real world.

For example, you might be asked about how scientists can tell people about an idea without being biased, or about the good and bad points of a certain type of model.

Working Scientifically is covered on pages 2-16.

You need to think about the information you've been given and use your scientific know-how to answer the question. Always read the question and any data you've been given really carefully before you start writing your answer.

Working Scientifically

The Scientific Method

This section <u>isn't</u> about how to 'do' science — but it does show you the way <u>most scientists</u> work.

Science is All About **Testing Hypotheses**

Scientists Make an **Observation**

1) Scientists <u>OBSERVE</u> (look at) something they don't understand, e.g. an illness.
2) They come up with a <u>possible explanation</u> for what they've observed.
3) This explanation is called a <u>HYPOTHESIS</u>.

Hundreds of years ago, we thought demons caused illness.

They **Test** Their Hypothesis

1) Next, they test whether the hypothesis is <u>right or not</u>.
2) They do this by making a <u>PREDICTION</u> — a statement based on the hypothesis that can be tested.
3) They then <u>TEST</u> this prediction by carrying out <u>experiments</u>.
4) If their prediction is <u>right</u>, this is <u>EVIDENCE</u> that their <u>hypothesis might be right</u> too.

Other Scientists Test the Hypothesis Too

1) Other scientists <u>check</u> the evidence — for example, they check that the experiment was carried out in a <u>sensible</u> way. This is called <u>PEER-REVIEW</u>.
2) Scientists then <u>share their results</u>, e.g. in scientific papers.
3) Other scientists carry out <u>more experiments</u> to test the hypothesis.
4) Sometimes these scientists will find <u>more evidence</u> that the <u>hypothesis is RIGHT</u>.
5) Sometimes they'll find <u>evidence</u> that shows the <u>hypothesis is WRONG</u>.

Then we thought it was caused by 'bad blood' (and treated it with leeches).

The Hypothesis is **Accepted** or **Rejected**

1) If <u>all the evidence</u> that's been found <u>supports</u> the <u>hypothesis</u>, it becomes an <u>ACCEPTED THEORY</u> and goes into <u>textbooks</u> for people to learn.
2) If the <u>evidence</u> shows that the hypothesis is <u>wrong</u>, scientists must:
   - <u>Change the hypothesis</u>, OR
   - Come up with a <u>new hypothesis</u>.

Now we know that illnesses that can be spread between people are due to microorganisms.

Scientific models are constantly being refined...

You can see just how much testing has to be done before something gets accepted as a theory. If scientists aren't busy testing their own hypothesis, then they're busy testing someone else's.

Models and Communication

Once scientists have made a <u>new discovery</u>, they <u>don't</u> just keep it to themselves. Oh no. Time to learn about how scientific discoveries are <u>communicated</u>, and the <u>models</u> that are used to represent theories.

Theories Can Involve Different Types of Models

1) A <u>model</u> is a <u>simple way</u> of <u>describing</u> or <u>showing</u> what's going on in <u>real life</u>.
2) Models can be used to <u>explain ideas</u> and <u>make predictions</u>. For example:

> The <u>'lock and key' model</u> of enzyme action is a simple way of showing how <u>enzymes</u> work. It can be used to explain why enzymes only work in particular reactions. (See p.42 for more.)

3) All models have <u>limits</u> — a single model <u>can't explain</u> everything about an idea.

It's Important to Tell People About Scientific Discoveries

1) Scientific discoveries can make a big difference to <u>people's lives</u>.
2) So scientists need to <u>tell the world</u> about their discoveries.
3) They might need to tell people to <u>change their habits</u>, e.g. stop smoking to protect against lung cancer.
4) They might also need to tell people about new <u>technologies</u>. For example:

> <u>Gene technologies</u> are used in <u>genetic engineering</u> to produce <u>genetically modified crops</u>. Information about these crops needs to be given to <u>farmers</u> who might <u>benefit</u> from growing them. The <u>general public</u> also needs to be told about these crops, so they can make <u>informed decisions</u> about the food they buy and eat.

Scientific Evidence can be Presented in a Biased Way

1) <u>Reports</u> about scientific discoveries in the <u>media</u> (e.g. newspapers or television) can be <u>misleading</u>.
2) The data might be <u>presented</u> in a way that's <u>not quite right</u> — or it might be <u>oversimplified</u>.
3) This means that people may not <u>properly understand</u> what the scientists found out.
4) People who want to make a point can also sometimes <u>present data</u> in a <u>biased way</u> (in a way that's <u>unfair</u> or <u>ignores</u> one side of the argument). For example:

- A <u>scientist</u> may talk a lot about <u>one particular relationship</u> in the data (and not mention others).
- A <u>newspaper article</u> might describe data <u>supporting</u> an idea without giving any evidence <u>against</u> it.

Companies can present biased data to help sell products...

Sometimes a company may only want you to see half of the story so they present the data in a <u>biased way</u>. For example, a medicines company may want to encourage you to buy their drugs. They might tell you about all the <u>positives</u>, but not report the results of any <u>unfavourable studies</u>.

Issues Created by Science

Science has helped us to <u>make progress</u> in loads of areas, from medicine to space travel. But science still has its <u>issues</u>. And it <u>can't answer everything</u>, as you're about to find out.

Scientific Developments are Great, but they can Raise Issues

1) Scientific developments include <u>new technologies</u> and <u>new advice</u>.
2) These developments can create <u>issues</u>. For example:

<u>Economic (money) issues:</u> Society <u>can't</u> always <u>afford</u> to do things scientists recommend, like spend money on green energy sources.

<u>Social (people) issues:</u> Decisions based on scientific evidence affect <u>people</u> — e.g. should alcohol be banned (to prevent health problems)?

<u>Personal issues:</u> Some decisions will affect <u>individuals</u> — e.g. people may be upset if a <u>wind farm</u> is built next to their house.

<u>Environmental issues:</u> <u>Human activity</u> often affects the <u>environment</u> — e.g. some people think that <u>genetically modified crops</u> (see p.137) could cause <u>environmental problems</u>.

Science Can't Answer Every Question — Especially Ethical Ones

1) At the moment scientists <u>don't agree</u> on some things — like what the Universe is made of.
2) This is because there <u>isn't</u> enough <u>data</u> to <u>support</u> the scientists' hypotheses.
3) But <u>eventually</u>, we probably <u>will</u> be able to answer these questions once and for all.
4) Experiments <u>can't tell us</u> whether something is <u>ethically right or wrong</u>. For example, whether it's right for people to use new drugs to help them do better in exams.
5) The best we can do is make a decision that <u>most people</u> are more or less happy to live by.

There are often issues with new scientific developments...

The trouble is, there's often <u>no clear right answer</u> where these issues are concerned. Different people have <u>different views</u>, depending on their priorities. These issues are full of <u>grey areas</u>.

Risk

Scientific discoveries are often great, but they can prove risky. With dangers all around, you've got to be aware of hazards — this includes how likely they are to cause harm and how serious the effects may be.

Nothing is Completely **Risk-Free**

1) A hazard is something that could cause harm.

2) All hazards have a risk attached to them — this is the chance that the hazard will cause harm.

3) New technology can bring new risks. E.g. scientists are creating technology to capture and store carbon dioxide. But if the carbon dioxide leaked out it could damage soil or water supplies. These risks need to be considered alongside the benefits of the technology, e.g. lower greenhouse gas emissions.

4) To make a decision about activities that involve hazards, we need to think about:
   - the chance of the hazard causing harm,
   - how bad the outcome (consequences) would be if it did.

People Make Their **Own Decisions** About Risk

1) Not all risks have the same consequences. For example, if you chop veg with a sharp knife you risk cutting your finger, but if you go scuba-diving you risk death.

2) Most people are happier to accept a risk if the consequences don't last long and aren't serious.

3) People tend to think familiar activities are low-risk. They tend to think unfamiliar activities are high-risk. But this isn't always true. For example:

   - Cycling on roads is often high-risk. But it's a familiar activity, so many people are happy to do it.
   - Air travel is actually pretty safe, but a lot of people think it is high-risk.

4) The best way to estimate the size of a risk is to look at data. E.g. you could estimate the risk of a driver crashing by recording how many people in a group of 100 000 drivers crashed their cars over a year.

The pros and cons of new technology must be weighed up...

The world's a dangerous place and it's impossible to rule out the chance of an accident altogether. But if you can recognise hazards and take steps to reduce the risks, you're more likely to stay safe.

Designing Investigations

Dig out your lab coat and dust down your safety goggles... it's <u>investigation time</u>.
Investigations include <u>lab experiments</u> and <u>studies</u> done in the <u>real world</u>.

Evidence Can Support or Disprove a Hypothesis

1) Scientists <u>observe</u> things and come up with <u>hypotheses</u> to explain them (see p.2).
   You need to be able to do the same. For example:

   > <u>Observation</u>: People have big feet and spots. <u>Hypothesis</u>: Having big feet causes spots.

2) To <u>find out</u> if your hypothesis is <u>right</u>, you need to do an <u>investigation</u> to gather evidence.

3) To do this, you need to use your hypothesis to make a <u>prediction</u> — something you think <u>will happen</u>
   that you can <u>test</u>. E.g. people who have bigger feet will have more spots.

4) Investigations are used to see if there are <u>patterns</u> or <u>relationships</u> between <u>two variables</u> (see below).

Make an Investigation a Fair Test By Controlling the Variables

1) In a lab experiment you usually <u>change one thing</u> (a variable)
   and <u>measure</u> how it affects <u>another thing</u> (another variable).

   > <u>EXAMPLE:</u> you might <u>change</u> the <u>concentration</u> of a reactant
   > and <u>measure</u> how it affects the <u>temperature change</u> of the reaction.

2) <u>Everything else</u> that could affect the results needs to <u>stay the same</u>.
   Then you know that the thing you're <u>changing</u> is the <u>only</u> thing that's affecting the results.

   > <u>EXAMPLE continued:</u> you need to keep the volume of the reactants the same.
   > If you don't, you won't know if any change in the temperature is caused by
   > the change in concentration, or the change in volume.

3) The variable that you <u>CHANGE</u> is called the <u>INDEPENDENT</u> variable.

4) The variable you <u>MEASURE</u> is called the <u>DEPENDENT</u> variable.

5) The variables that you <u>KEEP THE SAME</u> are called
   <u>CONTROL</u> variables.

6) Because you can't always control all the variables,
   you often need to use a <u>CONTROL EXPERIMENT</u>.

   > <u>EXAMPLE continued:</u>
   > Independent = concentration
   > Dependent = temperature
   > Control = volume of
   >   reactants, pH, etc.

7) This is an experiment that's kept under the <u>same conditions</u> as the rest of the investigation, but <u>doesn't</u>
   have anything <u>done</u> to it. This is so that you can see what happens when you don't change <u>anything</u>.

Evidence Needs to be Repeatable, Reproducible and Valid

1) <u>REPEATABLE</u> means that if the <u>same person</u> does the experiment again, they'll get <u>similar results</u>.
   To check your results are repeatable, <u>repeat</u> the readings <u>at least three times</u>.
   Then check the repeat results are all similar.

2) <u>REPRODUCIBLE</u> means that if <u>someone else</u> does the experiment, the results will still be <u>similar</u>.
   To make sure your results are reproducible, get <u>another person</u> to do the experiment too.

3) <u>VALID results</u> come from experiments that were designed to be a <u>fair test</u>.
   They're also repeatable and reproducible.

If data is repeatable and
reproducible, scientists are
more likely to trust it.

Designing Investigations

The **Bigger** the **Sample Size** the **Better**

1) Sample size is <u>how many things you test</u> in an investigation, e.g. 500 people or 20 types of metal.

2) The <u>bigger</u> the sample size the <u>better</u> — to <u>reduce</u> the chance of any <u>weird results</u>.

3) But scientists have to be <u>realistic</u> when choosing how big their sample should be. E.g. if you were studying how lifestyle affects weight it'd be great to study everyone in the UK (a huge sample), but it'd take ages and cost loads.

4) When you choose a sample, you need to make sure you've got a <u>range</u> of different people.

5) For example, both <u>men</u> and <u>women</u> with a range of <u>different ages</u>.

Your Data Should be **Accurate** and **Precise**

1) <u>ACCURATE results</u> are results that are <u>really close</u> to the <u>true answer</u>.

2) The accuracy of your results usually depends on your <u>method</u>. You need to make sure you're measuring the <u>right thing</u>.

3) You also need to make sure you <u>don't miss anything</u> that should be included in the measurements. For example:

> If you're measuring the <u>volume of gas</u> released by a reaction, make sure you <u>collect all the gas</u>.

4) <u>PRECISE results</u> are ones where the data is <u>all really close</u> to the <u>mean</u> (average) of your repeated results.

Repeat	Data set 1	Data set 2
1	12	11
2	14	17
3	13	14
Mean	<u>13</u>	<u>14</u>

Data set 1 is more precise than data set 2 — the results are all close to the mean (not spread out).

Your **Equipment** has to be **Right for the Job**

1) The <u>measuring equipment</u> you use has to be able to <u>accurately</u> measure the chemicals you're using. E.g. if you need to measure out 11 cm^3 of a liquid, use a <u>measuring cylinder</u> that can measure to 1 cm^3 — not 5 or 10 cm^3.

2) You also need to <u>set up the equipment properly</u>. For example, make sure your <u>mass balance</u> is set to <u>zero</u> before you start weighing things.

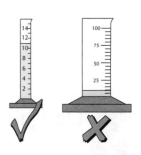

Designing Investigations

You Need to Look out for **Errors** and **Anomalous Results**

1) The results of your experiment will always <u>vary a bit</u> because of <u>RANDOM ERRORS</u> —
   for example, mistakes you might make while <u>measuring</u>.

2) You can <u>reduce</u> the effect of random errors by taking <u>repeat readings</u> and finding the <u>mean</u>.
   This will make your results <u>more precise</u>.

3) If a measurement is wrong by the <u>same amount every time</u>, it's called a <u>SYSTEMATIC ERROR</u>.
   For example:

   | If you measure from the <u>very end</u> of your <u>ruler</u> instead of from the <u>0 cm mark</u> every time, <u>all</u> your measurements would be a bit <u>small</u>. |

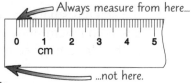

4) If you know you've made a systematic error, you might be able to <u>correct it</u>.
   For example, by adding a bit on to all your measurements.

5) Sometimes you get a result that <u>doesn't fit in</u> with the rest. This is called an <u>ANOMALOUS RESULT</u>.

6) You should try to <u>work out what happened</u>. If you do (e.g. you find out you measured
   something wrong) you can <u>ignore</u> it when processing your results (see next page).

Investigations Can Have **Hazards**

1) Hazards from science experiments include things like:

<u>microorganisms</u> (e.g. bacteria)	<u>chemicals</u>	<u>electricity</u>	<u>fire</u>
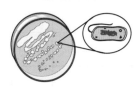	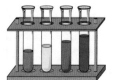		

2) When you <u>plan</u> an investigation you need to make sure that it's <u>safe</u>.

3) You should <u>identify</u> all the hazards that you might come across.

4) Then you should think of ways of <u>reducing the risks</u>. For example:

   - If you're working with <u>sulfuric acid</u>, always wear gloves and safety goggles.
     This will reduce the risk of the acid <u>burning</u> your skin and eyes.

   - If you're using a <u>Bunsen burner</u>, stand it on a heat proof mat.
     This will reduce the risk of starting a fire.

There's more on safety in experiments on page 168.

Designing an investigation is an involved process...

Collecting <u>data</u> is what investigations are all about. Designing a good investigation is really
important to make sure that any data collected is <u>accurate</u>, <u>precise</u>, <u>repeatable</u> and <u>reproducible</u>.

Processing Data

Processing your data means doing some <u>calculations</u> with it to make it <u>more useful</u>.

Data Needs to be Organised

1) <u>Tables</u> are useful for <u>organising data</u>.
2) When you draw a table <u>use a ruler</u>.
3) Make sure <u>each column</u> has a <u>heading</u> (including the <u>units</u>).

Test tube	Repeat 1 (cm³)	Repeat 2 (cm³)
A	28	37
B	47	51

There are Different Ways of Processing Your Data

1) When you've done repeats of an experiment you should always calculate the <u>mean</u> (a type of average).
2) You might also need to calculate the <u>range</u> (how spread out the data is).

EXAMPLE: **The results of an experiment to find the volume of gas produced in a reaction are shown in the table below. Calculate the mean volume and the range.**

Volume of gas produced (cm³)		
Repeat 1	Repeat 2	Repeat 3
28	37	32

1) To calculate the <u>mean</u>, <u>add together</u> all the data values. Then <u>divide</u> by the <u>total number</u> of values in the sample.

$(28 + 37 + 32) \div 3$
$= 32 \text{ cm}^3$

2) To calculate the <u>range</u>, <u>subtract</u> the <u>smallest</u> number from the <u>largest</u> number.

$37 - 28 = 9 \text{ cm}^3$

3) To find the <u>median</u>, put all your data in <u>order</u> from smallest to largest. The median is the <u>middle value</u>.
4) The number that appears <u>most often</u> is the <u>mode</u>.

E.g. if you have the data set: 1 2 1 1 3 4 2
The <u>median</u> is: 1 1 1 <u>2</u> 2 3 4. The <u>mode</u> is <u>1</u> because 1 appears most often.

If you have an even number of values, the median is halfway between the middle two values.

5) When calculating any of these values, always <u>ignore</u> any <u>anomalous results</u>.

Round to the Lowest Number of Significant Figures

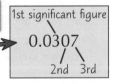
1st significant figure
0.0307
2nd   3rd

1) The <u>first significant figure</u> of a number is the first digit that's <u>not zero</u>.
2) The second and third significant figures come <u>straight after</u> (even if they're zeros).
3) In <u>any</u> calculation, you should round the answer to the <u>lowest number of significant figures</u> (s.f.) given.
4) If your calculation has more than one step, <u>only</u> round the <u>final</u> answer.

EXAMPLE: **A plant produces 10.2 cm³ of oxygen in 6.5 minutes whilst photosynthesising. Calculate the rate of photosynthesis.**

rate = 10.2 cm³ ÷ 6.5 min = 1.5692... = 1.6 cm³/min (2 s.f.)
            3 s.f.   2 s.f.   Final answer should be rounded to 2 s.f.

EXAM TIP

Don't forget your calculator...

In the exam you could be given some <u>data</u> and be expected to <u>process it</u> in some way. Make sure you keep an eye on <u>significant figures</u> in your answers and <u>always write down your working</u>.

Presenting Data

Once you've processed your data, e.g. by calculating the mean, you can present your results in a nice <u>chart</u> or <u>graph</u>. This will help you to <u>spot any patterns</u> in your data.

If Your Data Comes in **Categories**, Present it in a **Bar Chart**

If the independent variable comes in <u>clear categories</u> (e.g. blood group, types of metal) or can be <u>counted exactly</u> (e.g. number of protons) you should use a <u>bar chart</u> to display the data. Here's what to do:

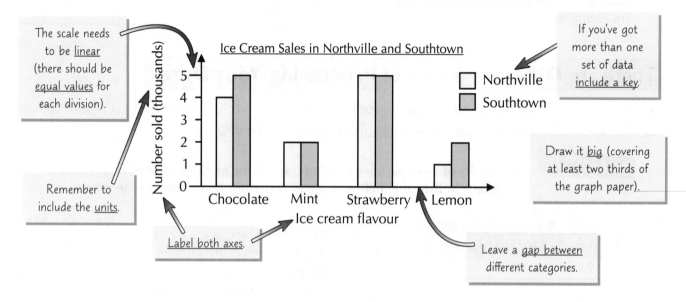

The scale needs to be <u>linear</u> (there should be <u>equal values</u> for each division).

Remember to include the <u>units</u>.

Label both axes.

If you've got more than one set of data <u>include a key</u>.

Draw it <u>big</u> (covering at least two thirds of the graph paper).

Leave a <u>gap between</u> different categories.

If Your Data is **Continuous**, Plot a **Graph**

If both variables can have any value <u>within a range</u> (e.g. length, volume) use a <u>graph</u> to display the data. Here are the rules for plotting points on a graph:

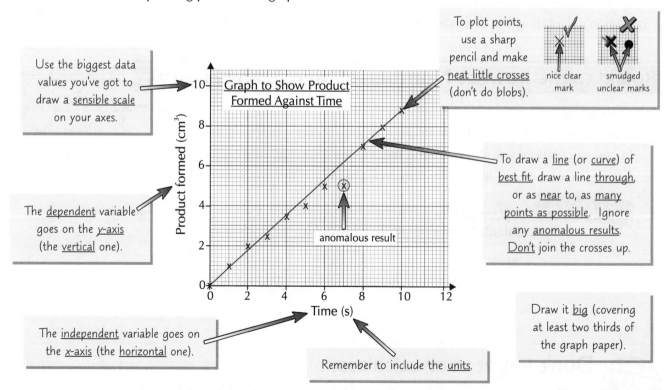

Use the biggest data values you've got to draw a <u>sensible scale</u> on your axes.

The <u>dependent</u> variable goes on the <u>y-axis</u> (the <u>vertical</u> one).

The <u>independent</u> variable goes on the <u>x-axis</u> (the <u>horizontal</u> one).

Remember to include the <u>units</u>.

To plot points, use a sharp pencil and make <u>neat little crosses</u> (don't do blobs).

nice clear mark

smudged unclear marks

To draw a <u>line</u> (or <u>curve</u>) of <u>best fit</u>, draw a line <u>through</u>, or as <u>near</u> to, as <u>many points as possible</u>. Ignore any <u>anomalous results</u>. <u>Don't</u> join the crosses up.

anomalous result

Draw it <u>big</u> (covering at least two thirds of the graph paper).

More on Graphs

Graph's aren't just fun to plot, they're also really useful for showing <u>trends</u> in your data.

You Can Calculate the **Rate** of a Reaction from the **Gradient** of a Graph

1) This is the <u>formula</u> you need to calculate the <u>gradient</u> (slope) of a graph:

$$\text{gradient} = \frac{\text{change in } y}{\text{change in } x}$$

2) You can use it to work out the <u>rate of a reaction</u> (how <u>quickly</u> the reaction happens).

EXAMPLE: **The graph shows the volume of gas produced in a reaction against time. Calculate the rate of reaction.**

1) To calculate the <u>gradient</u>, pick <u>two points</u> on the line that are easy to read. They should also be a <u>good distance</u> apart.

2) Draw a line <u>down</u> from the higher point. Then draw a line <u>across</u> from the other, to make a <u>triangle</u>.

3) The line drawn <u>down the side</u> of the triangle is the <u>change in y</u>. The line <u>across the bottom</u> is the <u>change in x</u>.

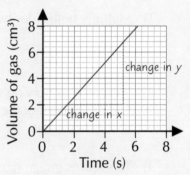

4) Read the x and y values of the points <u>off the graph</u> and work out the change in y and the change in x:

Change in y = 6.8 − 2.0 = 4.8 cm^3 Change in x = 5.2 − 1.6 = 3.6 s

To calculate a rate, the graph must have time on the x-axis.

5) Then put these numbers in the formula above to find the rate of the reaction:

$$\text{Rate} = \text{gradient} = \frac{\text{change in } y}{\text{change in } x} = \frac{4.8 \text{ cm}^3}{3.6 \text{ s}} = 1.3 \text{ cm}^3/\text{s}$$

The units are (units of y)/(units of x). cm^3/s can also be written as cm^3 s^{-1}.

Graphs Show the **Relationship** Between Two Variables

1) You can get <u>three</u> types of <u>correlation</u> (relationship) between variables:

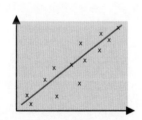

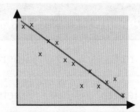

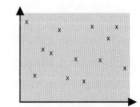

<u>POSITIVE correlation:</u> as one variable <u>increases</u> the other <u>increases</u>.

<u>INVERSE (negative) correlation:</u> as one variable <u>increases</u> the other <u>decreases</u>.

<u>NO correlation:</u> <u>no relationship</u> between the two variables.

2) A correlation <u>doesn't mean</u> the change in one variable is <u>causing</u> the change in the other (see page 14).

Graphs make it much easier to see relationships in data...

If you can't work out what kind of correlation a graph shows, just remember that an inverse correlation gives a line of best fit that slopes downwards, so it looks like the letter N (for <u>N</u>egative).

Rearranging Equations and Units

Graphs and maths skills are all very well, but the numbers don't mean much if you don't get the <u>units</u> right.

You Can **Rearrange** Equations

1) Equations show <u>relationships</u> between <u>variables</u>. For example, magnification = $\dfrac{\text{image size}}{\text{real size}}$.

2) The <u>subject</u> of an equation is the variable <u>by itself</u> on one side of the equals sign. So <u>magnification</u> is the <u>subject</u> in the equation above.

3) To <u>change</u> the <u>subject</u> of an equation do the same thing to <u>both sides</u> of the equation until you've got the subject you <u>want</u>.

> **EXAMPLE:** **Make image size the subject of the equation above.**
>
> 1) <u>Multiply</u> both sides by <u>real size</u>. magnification = $\dfrac{\text{image size}}{\text{real size}}$
>
> $\implies$ magnification × real size = $\dfrac{\text{image size × real size}}{\text{real size}}$
>
> 2) 'Real size' is now on the top <u>and</u> the bottom of the fraction, so it cancels out: magnification × real size = $\dfrac{\text{image size × real̶ ̶s̶i̶z̶e̶}}{\text{real̶ ̶s̶i̶z̶e̶}}$
>
> 3) This leaves <u>image size</u> by itself. So it's the <u>subject</u>: magnification × real size = image size

S.I. Units Are Used All Round the World

1) All scientists use the same <u>units</u> to measure their data.

2) These are <u>standard units</u>, called S.I. units.

3) Here are some S.I. units you might see:

Quantity	S.I. Base Unit
mass	kilogram, kg
length	metre, m
time	second, s
temperature	kelvin, K

S.I. units help scientists to compare data...

You can only really <u>compare</u> things if they're in the <u>same units</u>. E.g. if the rate of blood flow was measured in ml/min in one vein and in l/day in another vein, it'd be hard to know which was faster.

More on Units

You can <u>convert units</u>, which can save you from having to write a lot of 0's...

Different Units Help you to Write **Large** and **Small** Quantities

1) Quantities come in a huge <u>range</u> of sizes.

2) To make the size of numbers <u>easier to handle,</u> larger or smaller units are used.

3) Larger and smaller units are written as the <u>S.I. base unit</u> with a <u>little word</u> in <u>front</u> (a prefix). Here are some <u>examples</u> of <u>prefixes</u> and what they mean:

Kilogram is an exception. It's an S.I. unit with the prefix already on it.

Prefix	mega (M)	kilo (k)	deci (d)	centi (c)	milli (m)	micro (µ)
How it compares to the base unit	1 000 000 times bigger	1000 times bigger	10 times smaller	100 times smaller	1000 times smaller	1 000 000 times smaller

E.g. 1 <u>kilometre</u> is <u>1000</u> metres.

E.g. there are <u>1000</u> <u>millimetres</u> in 1 metre.

You Need to be Able to **Convert Between Units**

You need to know how to <u>convert</u> (change) one unit into another. Here are some useful conversions:

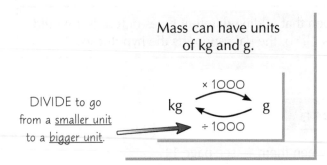

Mass can have units of kg and g.

DIVIDE to go from a <u>smaller unit</u> to a <u>bigger unit</u>.

× 1000

kg ⇄ g

÷ 1000

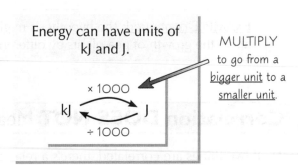

Energy can have units of kJ and J.

MULTIPLY to go from a <u>bigger unit</u> to a <u>smaller unit</u>.

× 1000

kJ ⇄ J

÷ 1000

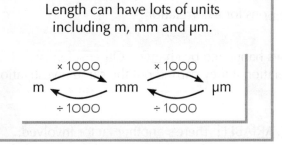

Length can have lots of units including m, mm and µm.

× 1000   × 1000

m ⇄ mm ⇄ µm

÷ 1000   ÷ 1000

Always make sure the values you put into an equation or formula have the right units.

EXAMPLE: **A seedling has grown 0.023 m in a week. How many mm has it grown?**

1 m = 1000 mm. So to convert from m (a bigger unit) to mm (a smaller unit) you need to <u>multiply</u> by 1000.

0.023 m × 1000 = 23 mm

MATHS TIP

To convert from bigger units to smaller units...

...you need to <u>multiply</u>, and to convert from <u>smaller units</u> to <u>bigger units</u>, you need to <u>divide</u>. Don't get this the wrong way round or you'll get answers that are far too big or far too small.

Drawing Conclusions

Once you've carried out an experiment and processed your data, it's time to work out what your data shows.

You Can Only Conclude What the Data Shows and NO MORE

1) To come to a conclusion, look at your data and say what pattern you see.

EXAMPLE: The table on the right shows the heights of pea plant seedlings grown for three weeks with different fertilisers.

Fertiliser	Mean growth / mm
A	13.5
B	19.5
No fertiliser	5.5

CONCLUSION: Pea plant seedlings grow taller over a three week period with fertiliser B than with fertiliser A.

2) It's important that the conclusion matches the data it's based on — it shouldn't go any further.

EXAMPLE continued: You can't conclude that any other type of plant grows taller with fertiliser B than with fertiliser A — the results could be totally different.

3) You also need to be able to use your results to justify your conclusion (i.e. back it up).

EXAMPLE continued: The pea plants grow 6 mm more on average with fertiliser B than with fertiliser A.

4) When writing a conclusion you need to say whether or not the data supports the original hypothesis:

EXAMPLE continued: The hypothesis might have been that adding different types of fertiliser would affect the growth of pea plants by different amounts. If so, the data supports the hypothesis.

Correlation DOES NOT Mean Cause

1) If two things are correlated, there's a relationship between them — see page 11.
2) But a correlation doesn't always mean that a change in one variable is causing the change in the other.
3) There are three possible reasons for a correlation:

1) CHANCE: The results happened by chance. Other scientists wouldn't get a correlation if they carried out the same investigation.

2) LINKED BY A 3RD VARIABLE: There's another factor involved.

E.g. there's a correlation between water temperature and shark attacks. They're linked by a third variable — the number of people swimming (more people swim when the water's hotter, which means you get more shark attacks).

3) CAUSE: Sometimes a change in one variable does cause a change in the other. You can only conclude this when you've controlled all the variables that could be affecting the result.

Uncertainty

Uncertainty is how sure you can really be about your data. There's a little bit of maths to do, and also a formula to learn. But don't worry too much — it's no more than a simple bit of subtraction and division.

Uncertainty is the Amount of Error Your Measurements Might Have

1) Measurements you make will have some uncertainty in them (i.e. they won't be completely perfect).

2) This can be due to random errors (see page 8). It can also be due to limits in what your measuring equipment can measure.

3) This means that the mean of your results will have some uncertainty to it.

4) You can calculate the uncertainty of a mean result using this equation:

$$\text{uncertainty} = \frac{\text{range}}{2}$$

The range is the largest value minus the smallest value (p.9).

5) The less precise your results are, the higher the uncertainty will be.

6) Uncertainties are shown using the '±' symbol.

EXAMPLE:

The table below shows the results of a respiration experiment to determine the volume of carbon dioxide produced. Calculate the uncertainty of the mean.

Repeat	1	2	3	mean
Volume of CO_2 produced (cm^3)	20.1	19.8	20.0	20.0

1) First work out the range:

Range = 20.1 − 19.8 = 0.300 cm^3

2) Use the range to find the uncertainty:

Uncertainty = range ÷ 2 = 0.300 ÷ 2 = 0.150 cm^3

So the uncertainty of the mean = 20.0 ± 0.150 cm^3

The smaller the uncertainty, the more precise your results...

Remember that equation for uncertainty. You never know when you might need it — you could be expected to use it in the exams. You need to make sure all the data is in the same units though. For example, if you had some measurements in metres, and some in centimetres, you'd need to convert them all into either metres or centimetres before you set about calculating uncertainty.

Evaluations

Hurrah! The end of another investigation. Well, now you have to work out all the things you did <u>wrong</u>. That's what <u>evaluations</u> are all about I'm afraid. Best get cracking with this page...

Evaluations — Describe **How** it Could be **Improved**

In an evaluation you look back over the whole investigation.

1) You should comment on the <u>method</u> — was it <u>valid</u>? Did you control all the other variables to make it a <u>fair test</u>?

2) Comment on the <u>quality</u> of the <u>results</u> — was there <u>enough evidence</u> to reach a valid <u>conclusion</u>? Were the results <u>repeatable</u>, <u>reproducible</u>, <u>accurate</u> and <u>precise</u>?

3) Were there any <u>anomalous</u> results? If there were <u>none</u> then <u>say so</u>. If there were any, try to <u>explain</u> them — were they caused by <u>errors</u> in measurement?

4) You should comment on the level of <u>uncertainty</u> in your results too.

5) Thinking about these things lets you say how <u>confident</u> you are that your conclusion is <u>right</u>.

6) Then you can suggest any <u>changes</u> to the <u>method</u> that would <u>improve</u> the quality of the results, so you could have <u>more confidence</u> in your conclusion.

7) For example, taking measurements at <u>narrower intervals</u> could give you a <u>more accurate result</u>. E.g.

- Say you do an experiment to find the <u>temperature</u> at which an enzyme <u>works best</u>.
- You take measurements at <u>30 °C</u>, <u>40 °C</u> and <u>50 °C</u>. The results show that the enzyme works best at <u>40 °C</u>.
- To get a more accurate result, you could <u>repeat</u> the experiment and take <u>more measurements around 40 °C</u>. You might then find that the enzyme actually works best at <u>42 °C</u>.

8) You could also make more <u>predictions</u> based on your conclusion. You could then carry out <u>further experiments</u> to test the new predictions.

Always look for ways to improve your investigations

So there you have it — <u>Working Scientifically</u>. Make sure you know this stuff like the back of your hand. It's not just in the lab or the field, when you're carrying out your groundbreaking <u>investigations</u>, that you'll need to know how to work scientifically. You can be asked about it in the <u>exams</u> as well. So swot up...

Cells

Cells are the <u>building blocks</u> of <u>every organism on the planet</u>.

Cells can be **Prokaryotic** or **Eukaryotic**

1) <u>All living things</u> are made of <u>cells</u>.

2) <u>Eukaryotic</u> cells are <u>complex</u>. All <u>animal</u> and <u>plant</u> cells are eukaryotic.

3) <u>Prokaryotic</u> cells are <u>smaller</u> and <u>simpler</u>. <u>Bacteria</u> are prokaryotic cells.

Plant and **Animal** Cells have **Similarities** and **Differences**

The different parts of a cell are called <u>subcellular structures</u>.

Animal Cells

Most <u>animal</u> cells have these subcellular structures:

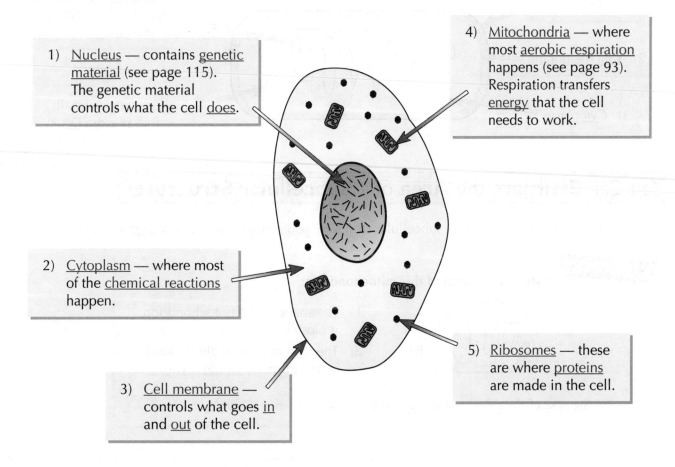

1) <u>Nucleus</u> — contains <u>genetic material</u> (see page 115). The genetic material controls what the cell <u>does</u>.

4) <u>Mitochondria</u> — where most <u>aerobic respiration</u> happens (see page 93). Respiration transfers <u>energy</u> that the cell needs to work.

2) <u>Cytoplasm</u> — where most of the <u>chemical reactions</u> happen.

3) <u>Cell membrane</u> — controls what goes <u>in</u> and <u>out</u> of the cell.

5) <u>Ribosomes</u> — these are where <u>proteins</u> are made in the cell.

Subcellular structures are all the different parts of a cell

Make sure you get to grips with the different <u>subcellular structures</u> that animal cells contain before you move on to the next page. There are more subcellular structures coming up that you <u>need to know</u>...

Cells

Plant Cells

Plant cells usually have all the bits that animal cells have.
They also have:

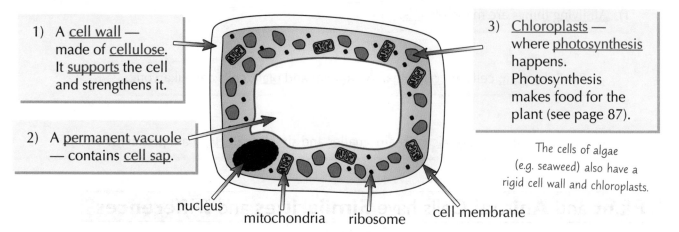

1) A cell wall — made of cellulose. It supports the cell and strengthens it.

2) A permanent vacuole — contains cell sap.

3) Chloroplasts — where photosynthesis happens. Photosynthesis makes food for the plant (see page 87).

The cells of algae (e.g. seaweed) also have a rigid cell wall and chloroplasts.

nucleus   mitochondria   ribosome   cell membrane

Bacterial Cells Have These Subcellular Structures:

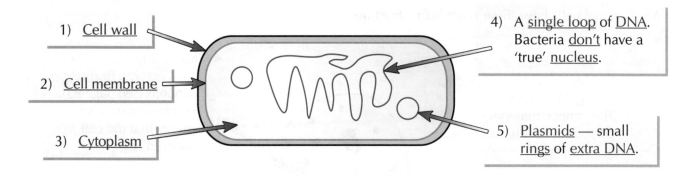

1) Cell wall

2) Cell membrane

3) Cytoplasm

4) A single loop of DNA. Bacteria don't have a 'true' nucleus.

5) Plasmids — small rings of extra DNA.

You Can Estimate the Area of a Subcellular Structure

If you want to estimate the area of a subcellular structure, you should treat it like a regular shape:

EXAMPLE:

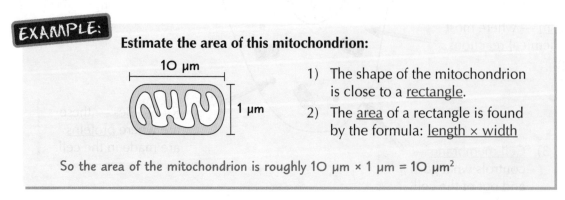

Estimate the area of this mitochondrion:

10 µm

1 µm

1) The shape of the mitochondrion is close to a rectangle.

2) The area of a rectangle is found by the formula: length × width

So the area of the mitochondrion is roughly 10 µm × 1 µm = 10 µm²

There's quite a bit to learn in biology — but that's life, I guess...

REVISION TIP On these pages are a typical animal cell, plant cell and bacterial cell. Make sure you're familiar with all their structures. A good way to check that you know what all the bits and pieces are is to copy out the diagrams and see if you can remember all the labels. No cheating.

Microscopy

Microscopes are pretty important for biology. So here are a couple of pages all about them...

Microscopes **Magnify** Things (Make Them Look **Bigger**)

1) The ways we can use microscopes have developed over the years.
This is because technology and knowledge have improved.

See the next page for how to use a light microscope.

2) Light microscopes can be used to look at cells.
They let us see large subcellular structures (like the nucleus).

3) Electron microscopes have a higher resolution than light microscopes
— they show things in more detail.

4) Electron microscopes also have a higher magnification than light microscopes.
They can let us see really small things like ribosomes and plasmids.

5) Electron microscopes were invented after light microscopes.
They helped scientists understand more about subcellular structures.

You Need to be Able to Use the **Formula** for **Magnification**

Magnification is how many times bigger the image is than the real thing.
You can work out the magnification of an image using this formula:

$$\text{magnification} = \frac{\text{image size}}{\text{real size}}$$

Image size and real size should have the same units.

EXAMPLE:

**The width of a cell is 0.02 mm. The width of its image under a microscope is 8 mm.
What magnification was used to view the cell?**

magnification = 8 mm ÷ 0.02 mm = × 400

You Can Write Numbers in **Standard Form**

Standard form is useful for writing very big or very small numbers in a simpler way.

EXAMPLE:  **Write 0.0025 mm in standard form.**

1) The first number needs to be between 1 and 10
so the decimal point needs to move after the '2'.

0.0025 → 2.5
1 2 3

2) Count how many places the decimal point has moved
— this is the power of 10.

The decimal point
has moved 3 places = 10^3

3) The power of 10 is positive if the decimal point is moved
to the left. It's negative if the decimal point has moved to the right.
Here, the decimal point has moved right, so it needs a minus sign.

2.5×10^{-3}

MATHS TIP

Standard form saves you from having to write a lot of zeros

Remember, when you're writing a number in standard form, the bit before the '×' sign has to
be smaller than 10, but can't be smaller than 1. You've got to move the decimal point to just
after the first digit that's not a zero. E.g. 342 000 is 3.42×10^5, and 0.0009513 is 9.513×10^4.

 **PRACTICAL** # Microscopy

So you know what microscopes <u>do</u>... now you need to know how to <u>use</u> one.

You Need to **Prepare** Your **Slide**

Lots of different animal and plant cells can be looked at under a light microscope.

1) Add a <u>drop of water</u> to the middle of a clean slide.

2) Cut up an onion and take off one <u>layer</u>.

3) Use <u>tweezers</u> to peel off some <u>epidermal tissue</u> (the clear 'skin') from the <u>bottom</u> of the layer.

4) Using the tweezers, place the skin into the <u>water</u> on the slide.

5) Add a drop of <u>iodine solution</u>. Iodine solution is a <u>stain</u>. Stains can make different parts of a cell <u>easier to see</u>.

6) Place a <u>cover slip</u> on top. Try <u>not</u> to get any <u>air bubbles</u> under it.

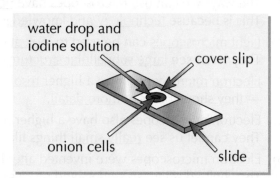

Know the Parts of a **Light Microscope**

To look at your prepared slides, you need to know how to use a light microscope. Here are the main parts you'll use:

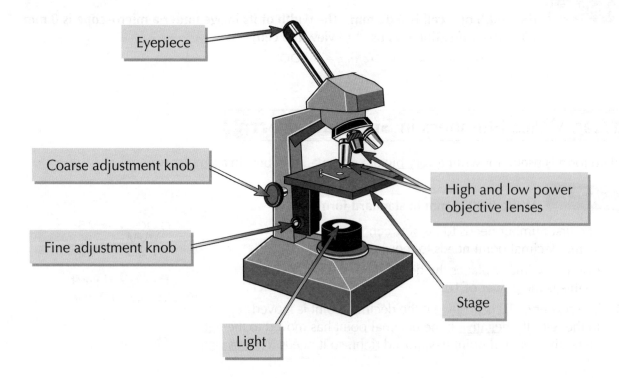

Stains can make subcellular structures easier to see

Carry on to the next page for <u>how to use</u> the microscope above to view your specimen.

Microscopy

Use a **Light Microscope** to Look at Your **Slide**

1) Clip the <u>slide</u> onto the <u>stage</u>.

2) Select the <u>objective lens</u> with the lowest magnification.

3) Use the <u>coarse adjustment knob</u> to move the stage up to <u>just below</u> the objective lens.

4) Look down the <u>eyepiece</u>. Move the stage downwards until the image is <u>roughly in focus</u>.

5) Move the <u>fine adjustment knob</u>, until you get a <u>clear image</u> of what's on the slide.

6) If you want a bigger image, use an <u>objective lens</u> with a <u>higher magnification</u> and refocus.

Draw Your Observations **Neatly** with a **Pencil**

1) You should use a <u>pencil</u> with a <u>sharp point</u> to draw <u>what you see</u> under the microscope.

2) Use <u>smooth lines</u> to draw the <u>outlines</u> of the <u>main features</u> (e.g. nucleus, chloroplasts).

3) <u>Don't</u> do any <u>shading</u> or <u>colouring in</u>.

4) <u>Label</u> the features with <u>straight lines</u>. Make sure the lines <u>don't cross over</u> each other.

5) The drawing should take up <u>at least half</u> the space available.

6) Include a <u>title</u> and a <u>scale</u>.

7) Write down the <u>magnification</u> that it was observed under.

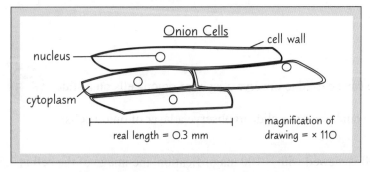

You can measure the real size of the cells using a
ruler that fits onto your microscope (see p.166).

Your microscope might look a bit different

The appearance of light microscopes can <u>vary</u> (e.g. they might have two eyepieces rather than one) but they should have the <u>same basic features</u> shown on the previous page.

Warm-Up & Exam Questions

So, hopefully you've read the last five pages. But could you cope if a question on cells or microscopes came up in the exam? See what happens when you try out these questions...

Warm-Up Questions

1) Name the subcellular structures where aerobic respiration takes place.
2) Give two ways in which animal cells are different from plant cells.
3) True or false? Bacterial cells have a nucleus.
4) What type of microscope should be used to look at ribosomes and plasmids?
5) Write the number 0.00045 μm in standard form.

Exam Questions

1   Which of the following cells is an example of a prokaryotic cell? Tick **one** box. (Grade 3-4)

☐ bacterial cell   ☐ animal cell   ☐ plant cell   ☐ sperm cell

[1 mark]

2   **Figure 1** shows a typical plant cell. (Grade 3-4)

Figure 1

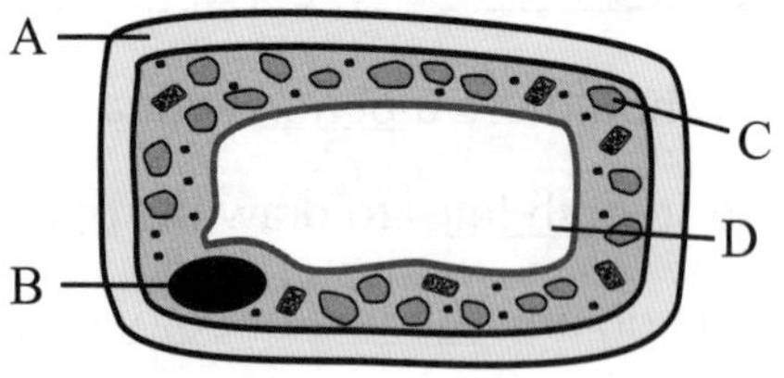

2.1   Which label points to a chloroplast? Tick **one** box.

☐ A   ☐ B   ☐ C   ☐ D

[1 mark]

2.2   What is the function of a chloroplast? Tick **one** box.

☐ allows photosynthesis to take place   ☐ contains genetic material   ☐ contains cell sap

[1 mark]

2.3   **Figure 1** also shows ribosomes.
What is the function of a ribosome? Tick **one** box.

☐ aerobic respiration   ☐ making proteins   ☐ storing extra DNA

[1 mark]

PRACTICAL

3   A light microscope can be used to observe a layer of onion cells on a slide. (Grade 4-5)

3.1*   Describe how you would prepare a slide to observe a layer of onion cells.

[4 marks]

3.2   When the onion cell is viewed with × 100 magnification, the image of the cell is 7.5 mm wide.

Calculate the real width of the onion cell in micrometres (μm). Complete the following steps.

Calculate the real width in mm using the formula: $\text{real size} = \dfrac{\text{image size}}{\text{magnification}}$

Convert mm to μm.

[2 marks]

Topic 1 — Cell Biology

Cell Differentiation and Specialisation

Cells <u>don't</u> all look the <u>same</u>. They have <u>different structures</u> to suit their <u>different functions</u>.

Specialised Cells are Cells that Carry Out a Specific Function

1) The process by which cells <u>change</u> to become <u>specialised</u> is called <u>differentiation</u>.

2) As cells change, they develop <u>different subcellular structures</u>.
They turn into <u>different types of cells</u>. This allows them to carry out <u>specific functions</u>.

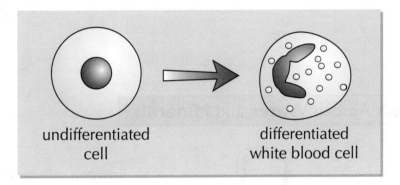

undifferentiated cell → differentiated white blood cell

3) Most differentiation occurs as an organism <u>develops</u>.

4) Most <u>animal</u> cells can only differentiate at an <u>early stage</u> of the animal's life.

5) But lots of <u>plant</u> cells can differentiate for the <u>whole</u> of the plant's life.

6) The cells that differentiate in <u>adult animals</u> are mainly used for <u>repairing</u> and <u>replacing cells</u>.

7) Some cells are <u>undifferentiated</u> — they are called <u>stem cells</u>.
There's more about them on pages 25-26.

There Are Many Examples of Specialised Cells...

Sperm Cells Take the Male DNA to the Egg

1) A sperm cell has a <u>tail</u> to help it <u>swim</u> to the egg.

2) It has a lot of <u>mitochondria</u> (see p.17).
These provide <u>energy</u> for swimming.

Nerve Cells Carry Electrical Signals Around the Body

1) Nerve cells are <u>long</u> to cover <u>more distance</u> in the body.

2) They have <u>branches</u> at the end to <u>connect</u> to other nerve cells.

Cell Specialisation

Muscle Cells Contract (Shorten)

1) Muscle cells are <u>long</u> so they have space to <u>contract</u>.

2) They have <u>lots of mitochondria</u>. These provide <u>energy</u> for contracting.

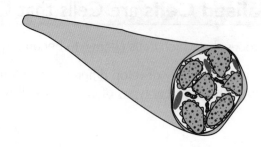

Root Hair Cells Absorb Water and Minerals

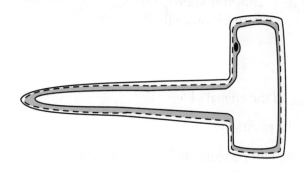

1) Root hair cells grow into long "<u>hairs</u>" that stick out into the soil.

2) This gives the plant a <u>big surface area</u> for absorbing <u>water</u> and <u>mineral ions</u> from the soil.

Phloem Cells Transport Food and Xylem Cells Transport Water

1) <u>Phloem</u> and <u>xylem cells</u> form phloem and xylem <u>tubes</u>.

2) To form the tubes, the cells are <u>long</u> and joined <u>end to end</u>.

3) Xylem cells are <u>hollow</u> and phloem cells have <u>very few</u> subcellular structures. So there's lots of space inside the cells for stuff to <u>flow through</u> them.

phloem   xylem

There's more about phloem and xylem on page 68.

Cells have the same basic bits but are specialised for their function

Not all cells contain <u>all</u> of the bits shown on pages 17-18. This is because some specialised cells don't have a use for certain subcellular structures — it depends on their <u>function</u>. For example, root hair cells grow <u>underground</u> in the soil. They <u>don't need chloroplasts</u> because they don't photosynthesise.

Stem Cells

Stem cell research has exciting <u>possibilities</u>, but <u>not everyone agrees</u> with some of the uses of stem cells.

Stem Cells can Differentiate into Different Types of Cells

1) Cells <u>differentiate</u> (change) to become <u>specialised</u> for their job (see page 23).

2) <u>Undifferentiated</u> cells are called <u>stem cells</u>.

3) Stem cells can produce lots <u>more</u> undifferentiated cells and differentiate into <u>different types of cell</u>.

4) Stem cells found in early <u>human embryos</u> are called <u>embryonic stem cells</u>.

5) Embryonic stem cells can turn into <u>any</u> kind of cell at all.

6) <u>Adults</u> also have stem cells. They're only in <u>certain places</u> in the body, like <u>bone marrow</u> (a tissue inside bones).

7) Adult stem cells can <u>only</u> produce <u>certain types</u> of specialised cell, e.g. blood cells.

8) Stem cells from embryos and bone marrow can be <u>cloned</u> (copied) in a lab. The cloned cells can be used in <u>medicine</u> or <u>research</u>.

An embryo is an unborn baby at an early stage of growth.

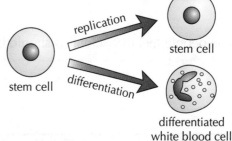

Stem Cells May Be Able to Cure Many Diseases

1) <u>Embryonic stem cells</u> could be used to <u>replace faulty cells</u> in sick people.

> E.g. you could make <u>nerve cells</u> for people with <u>paralysis</u> (where they can't move part of the body due to an injury to their spine) or <u>insulin-producing cells</u> for people with <u>diabetes</u> (see page 108).

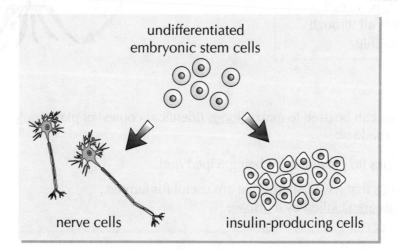

2) It's possible to <u>make an embryo</u> that has the <u>same genes</u> as a <u>patient</u>. This is called <u>therapeutic cloning</u>.

3) This means that the <u>stem cells</u> from the embryo <u>wouldn't</u> be <u>rejected</u> by the patient's body.

4) However, there are <u>risks</u> involved in using stem cells in medicine. For example, the stem cells could be <u>infected</u> with a <u>virus</u>. The virus could be <u>passed on</u> to a patient and make them <u>sicker</u>.

Stem Cells

Some People Are **Against Stem Cell Research**

1) Some people feel embryos <u>shouldn't</u> be used for research because each one could be a <u>human life</u>.

2) Others think that <u>curing patients</u> who are <u>suffering</u> is <u>more important</u> than the rights of embryos.

3) They argue that the embryos used in the research are usually <u>unwanted ones</u> from <u>fertility clinics</u>. If they weren't used for research, they would probably just be <u>destroyed</u>.

4) Some people feel that scientists should be finding <u>other sources</u> of stem cells.

Stem Cells Can Produce **Identical Plants**

1) Plants have tissues called <u>meristems</u>. Meristems are where <u>growth</u> occurs — in the tips of <u>roots</u> and <u>shoots</u>.

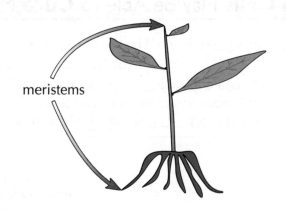

meristems

2) The meristems contain <u>stem cells</u> that can differentiate into <u>any type</u> of plant cell. They can do this all through the plant's <u>entire life</u>.

3) These stem cells can be used to make <u>clones</u> (identical copies) of plants <u>quickly</u> and <u>cheaply</u>. Clones can be made of:

- <u>rare species</u> (to prevent them being wiped out).

- <u>crop plants</u> that have <u>features</u> that are useful for farmers, e.g. plants <u>aren't killed</u> by a <u>disease</u>.

Getting stem cells from other places would avoid the disagreements

Scientists are looking into ways of getting human stem cells without using embryos. Whatever your opinion of stem cell research is, it's good to know what their <u>uses</u> are and the arguments <u>for</u> and <u>against</u> using them.

Chromosomes and Mitosis

In order to survive and grow, our cells have got to be able to <u>divide</u>. And that means our DNA does as well...

Chromosomes Contain Genetic Information

1) The <u>nucleus</u> of a cell contains <u>chromosomes</u>.

2) Chromosomes are <u>coiled up</u> lengths of <u>DNA molecules</u>.

3) Each chromosome carries a <u>large number</u> of genes.

4) Different genes <u>control</u> the development of different <u>characteristics</u>, e.g. hair colour.

5) <u>Body cells</u> normally have <u>two copies</u> of each <u>chromosome</u>.

6) There are <u>23 pairs of chromosomes</u> in a human cell.

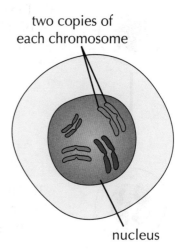

two copies of each chromosome

nucleus

The Cell Cycle Makes New Cells

1) <u>Body cells</u> in <u>multicellular organisms</u> (e.g. like you, me or a plant) <u>divide</u> to make new cells. This is part of a series of stages called the <u>cell cycle</u>.

2) The stage of the cell cycle when the cell <u>divides</u> is called <u>mitosis</u>.

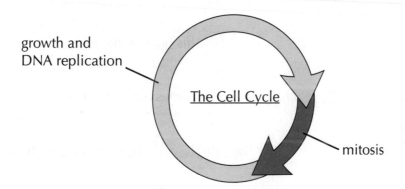

growth and DNA replication

The Cell Cycle

mitosis

3) Multicellular organisms use <u>mitosis</u> to <u>grow</u> and <u>develop</u>.

4) You need to know about the main stages of the <u>cell cycle</u> shown on the next page.

The cell cycle is important for growth and repair

When a cell goes through the cell cycle, you end up with <u>two cells</u> where you originally had just one. The body <u>controls</u> which cells divide and when — if this control <u>fails</u>, it can result in <u>cancer</u> (see page 65).

Chromosomes and Mitosis

There are two main stages of the <u>cell cycle</u>...

Growth and DNA Replication

Before it divides:

1) The cell <u>grows</u> and <u>increases</u> the amount of <u>subcellular structures</u> such as <u>ribosomes</u> and <u>mitochondria</u> (see page 17).

2) The DNA is <u>replicated</u> (copied) — so there's one copy for each new cell.

3) The DNA forms <u>X-shaped</u> chromosomes. Each 'arm' of the chromosome is an <u>exact copy</u> of the other.

The <u>left arm</u> has the same DNA as the <u>right arm</u> of the chromosome.

Mitosis

The cell is now ready for <u>dividing</u>...

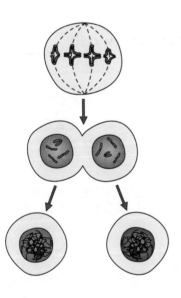

4) The chromosomes <u>line up</u> at the centre of the cell.

5) The <u>two arms</u> of each chromosome are <u>pulled apart</u> to <u>opposite ends</u> of the cell.

6) This <u>divides</u> the <u>nucleus</u>.

7) Each set of chromosomes become the <u>nucleus</u> of a new cell.

8) The <u>cytoplasm</u> and <u>cell membrane</u> divide.

The cell has now produced <u>two new cells</u>.
- They both contain the <u>same DNA</u> — they're <u>identical</u>.
- They're also <u>identical</u> to the <u>original cell</u>.

Mitosis produces two identical cells

Mitosis can seem tricky at first. But don't worry — just go through it slowly, one step at a time. This type of division produces <u>identical cells</u>, but there's another type which doesn't... (see page 118).

Warm-Up & Exam Questions

There's only one way to do well in the exam — learn the facts and then practise lots of exam questions to see what it'll be like on the big day. We couldn't have made it easier for you — so do it.

Warm-Up Questions

1) What is the name of the process where cells become specialised for their job?
2) Describe how a root hair cell is specialised for its function.
3) How many copies of each chromosome does a normal body cell have?
4) Where in the cell are chromosomes found?
5) True or false? The cells produced in mitosis are genetically identical.

Exam Questions

1 Draw **one** line from each cell type to its adaptation.

Cell type	Adaptation
Sperm cell	Many mitochondria to provide energy for contracting
	Very few subcellular structures, so there is more space inside the cell
Nerve cell	A tail for swimming
Muscle cell	Branches to connect to other cells

[3 marks]

2 Stem cells are cells produced by both plants and animals that can develop into any type of cell.

2.1 Draw **two** arrows on **Figure 1** to show two places where stem cells are produced in plants.

Figure 1

[2 marks]

2.2 Describe **one** way that plant stem cells can be used by farmers to increase crop yields.

[2 marks]

2.3 Stem cells might be useful for the treatment of human diseases.
Give **one** health condition that could possibly be treated with stem cells.

[1 mark]

Diffusion

Diffusion is really important in living organisms — it's how a lot of substances get in and out of cells.

Don't Be Put Off by the Fancy Word

1) "Diffusion" is the movement of particles from where there are lots of them to where there are fewer of them.

2) You have to learn this fancy way of saying it:

> DIFFUSION is the SPREADING OUT of particles from an area of HIGHER CONCENTRATION to an area of LOWER CONCENTRATION.

3) Diffusion happens in solutions and gases.
   For example, the smell of perfume diffuses through the air in a room:

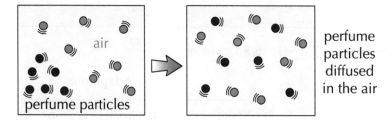

perfume particles diffused in the air

4) The difference in concentration is called the concentration gradient.
   The bigger the difference in concentration, the faster the diffusion rate.

5) A higher temperature will also give a faster diffusion rate.
   This is because the particles have more energy, so move around faster.

Cell Membranes Are Kind of Clever...

Oxygen is needed for aerobic respiration — see page 93.

1) Cell membranes let stuff diffuse in and out of the cell.

2) Only very small molecules can fit through cell membranes, e.g. oxygen, glucose, amino acids and water.

3) Big molecules like starch and proteins can't fit through the membrane:

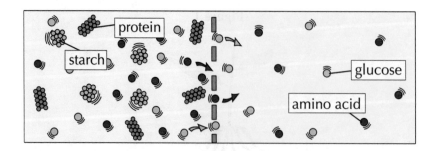

4) Molecules flow through the membrane from where there's a higher concentration (a lot of them) to where there's a lower concentration (not such a lot of them).

5) They actually move both ways — but if there are a lot more particles on one side of the membrane, there's a net (overall) movement from that side.

6) The larger the surface area of the membrane, the faster the diffusion rate.
   This is because more particles can pass through at the same time.

Osmosis

If you've got your head round <u>diffusion</u>, osmosis will be a <u>breeze</u>.
If not, have another look at the previous page...

Osmosis is the Movement of **Water Molecules**

<u>OSMOSIS</u> is the <u>movement of water molecules</u> across a <u>partially permeable membrane</u> from a <u>less concentrated</u> solution to a <u>more concentrated</u> solution.

1) A <u>partially permeable</u> membrane is just one with very small holes in it.

2) <u>Tiny molecules</u> (like water) can <u>pass through</u> it, but <u>bigger</u> molecules (e.g. sucrose) <u>can't</u>.

3) Water molecules actually pass <u>both ways</u> through the membrane during <u>osmosis</u>.

4) But overall, the water molecules move from the <u>less concentrated</u> solution (where there are lots of water molecules) to the <u>more concentrated</u> solution (where there are fewer water molecules).

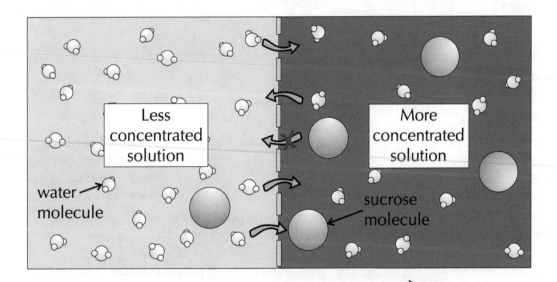

Less concentrated solution

More concentrated solution

water molecule

sucrose molecule

Overall movement of water molecules

5) This means the <u>more concentrated solution</u> gets <u>more dilute</u>.

6) The water acts like it's trying to "<u>even up</u>" the concentration either side of the membrane.

Diffusion is movement from where there's lots to where there's few...

...so osmosis is really just a fancy word for the <u>diffusion of water molecules</u>. It's simple really.

Osmosis

There's an <u>experiment</u> you can do to show osmosis at work.

You can **Observe** the Effect of **Sugar Solutions** on **Plant Tissue**

1) First, cut up a <u>potato</u> into cylinders with the <u>same length and width</u>.

2) Then get two beakers — one with <u>pure water</u> and another with a <u>very concentrated sugar solution</u> (e.g. 1 mol/dm³).

3) You can also have a few other beakers with <u>less concentrated sugar solutions</u> (e.g. 0.2 mol/dm³, 0.4 mol/dm³, etc).

4) Measure the <u>mass</u> of each potato cylinder, then put <u>one</u> in each beaker.

5) Leave the potato cylinders for <u>twenty four hours</u>.

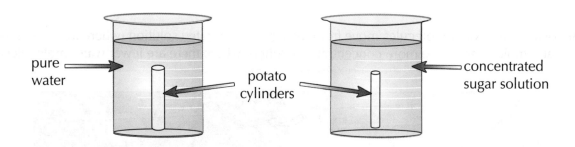

pure water   potato cylinders   concentrated sugar solution

6) Then take them out and <u>dry</u> them with a paper towel.

7) Measure their masses <u>again</u>.

You could also do this experiment using different concentrations of salt solution. You should see similar results.

8) If the <u>mass has increased</u>, water has moved <u>into</u> the potato cells.
   If the <u>mass has decreased</u>, water has moved <u>out</u> of the potato cells.

9) You can calculate the <u>percentage change in mass</u> for each potato cylinder — see p.172. This means you can <u>compare</u> the <u>effects</u> of each sugar solution.

10) The only thing you should <u>change</u> in this experiment is the <u>concentration</u> of the <u>sugar solution</u>. <u>Everything else</u> (e.g. volume of solution, temperature, time, type of sugar used) should <u>stay the same</u>.

Water always moves into the more concentrated solution

That's why it's bad to drink sea-water. The high <u>salt</u> content means you end up with a much <u>lower water concentration</u> in your blood and tissue fluid than in your cells. All the water is sucked out of your cells by osmosis and they <u>shrivel and die</u>. So next time you're stranded at sea, remember this...

Active Transport

Sometimes substances need to be absorbed from an area where they are in <u>low concentration</u> into an area where they are in <u>high concentration</u>. This happens by a process called <u>active transport</u>.

Root Hairs Take In **Minerals** and **Water**

1) Plant roots are covered in <u>millions</u> of <u>root hair cells</u>.

2) These cells <u>stick out</u> into the soil.

3) The "hairs" give the roots a <u>large surface area</u>.

4) This is useful for absorbing <u>water</u> and <u>mineral ions</u> from the soil.

5) Plants <u>need</u> mineral ions for <u>healthy growth</u>.

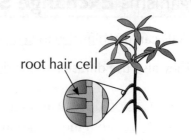

root hair cell

Root Hairs Take in Minerals Using **Active Transport**

1) The concentration of minerals is usually <u>higher</u> in the <u>root hair cells</u> than in the <u>soil</u> around them.

2) So the root hair cells <u>can't</u> use <u>diffusion</u> to take up minerals from the soil.

3) They use <u>active transport</u> instead.

4) Active transport allows the plant to absorb minerals from a very <u>dilute</u> solution in the soil — it moves the minerals <u>against</u> the <u>concentration gradient</u>.

5) But active transport needs <u>ENERGY</u> from <u>respiration</u> to make it work.

Water is taken into root hair cells by osmosis (see page 31).

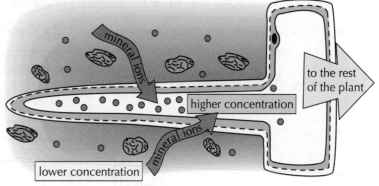

mineral ions

higher concentration

to the rest of the plant

lower concentration

We Need **Active Transport** to Stop Us Starving

1) The body needs to <u>absorb nutrients</u> (e.g. glucose and amino acids) from <u>food</u> to <u>survive</u>.

2) The nutrients have to move from the <u>gut</u> into the <u>blood</u>.

3) When there's a <u>higher concentration</u> of nutrients in the gut, they <u>diffuse</u> into the blood.

4) Sometimes there's a <u>lower concentration</u> of nutrients in the gut than there is in the blood.

5) The body uses <u>active transport</u> to move the nutrients (like glucose) from a <u>lower concentration</u> in the <u>gut</u> to a <u>higher concentration</u> in the <u>blood</u>.

6) This means <u>glucose</u> can be taken into the blood <u>against</u> the concentration gradient. The glucose is then transported to <u>cells</u>, where it's used for <u>respiration</u> (see page 93).

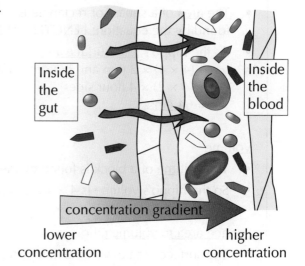

Inside the gut

Inside the blood

concentration gradient

lower concentration

higher concentration

Active transport uses energy

An important difference between <u>active transport</u> and <u>diffusion</u> is that active transport uses <u>energy</u>.

Exchanging Substances

How easily stuff <u>moves</u> between an <u>organism</u> and its <u>environment</u> depends on its <u>surface area to volume ratio</u>.

Organisms **Exchange Substances** with their **Environment**

1) Cells can use <u>diffusion</u> to <u>take in</u> substances from the <u>environment</u>, such as <u>oxygen</u>.

2) They also use diffusion to <u>get rid</u> of <u>waste products</u>, such as:

- <u>Carbon dioxide</u> (from <u>respiration</u>).
- <u>Urea</u> (from the <u>breakdown</u> of <u>proteins</u>) — urea diffuses from <u>cells</u> into the <u>blood plasma</u> (see p.54). It is then removed from the body by the <u>kidneys</u>.

3) How <u>easy</u> it is for an organism to <u>exchange</u> (swap) substances with its environment depends on the organism's <u>surface area to volume ratio</u>.

You Can **Calculate** an Organism's **Surface Area to Volume Ratio**

1) A <u>ratio</u> shows <u>how big</u> one value is <u>compared</u> to another.

2) So a <u>surface area to volume ratio</u> shows how big a shape's <u>surface</u> is compared to its <u>volume</u>.

E.g. a <u>2 cm × 4 cm × 4 cm block</u> can be used to <u>estimate</u> the surface area to volume ratio of a <u>hippo</u>:

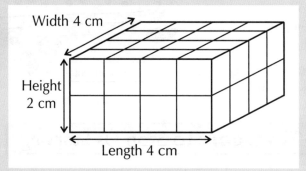

Width 4 cm

Height 2 cm

Length 4 cm

<u>Surface area</u>

- The <u>area</u> of a square or rectangle is found by the equation: LENGTH × WIDTH.
- So the hippo's <u>total surface area</u> is:
    (4 × 4) × 2 (top and bottom surfaces)
    + (4 × 2) × 4 (four sides)
    = <u>64 cm²</u>.

<u>Volume</u>

- The <u>volume</u> of a block is found by the equation: LENGTH × WIDTH × HEIGHT.
- So the hippo's <u>volume</u> is 4 × 4 × 2 = <u>32 cm³</u>.

<u>Surface area to volume ratio</u>

- The surface area to volume ratio (<u>SA : V</u>) of the hippo can be written as <u>64 : 32</u>.
- To get the ratio so that volume is equal to <u>one</u>, <u>divide both sides</u> of the ratio by the <u>volume</u>.

    64 ÷ 32 = 2   32 ÷ 32 = 1   So the SA : V of the hippo is <u>2 : 1</u>.

Exchanging Substances

Now for some more on <u>surface area to volume ratios</u>, and why they're important in biology...

Larger Objects Usually Have Smaller Surface Area to Volume Ratios

1) A <u>1 cm × 1 cm × 1 cm block</u> can be used to
   estimate the surface area to volume ratio of a <u>mouse</u>.

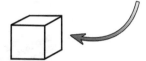

   It's found that the SA : V of the mouse is <u>6 : 1</u>.

2) The <u>larger</u> the organism, the <u>smaller</u> its surface area is compared to its volume.

> <u>Example:</u> The <u>surface area</u> of the <u>mouse</u> is <u>six times</u> its <u>volume</u>.
> The <u>surface area</u> of the <u>hippo</u> (see previous page) is only <u>two times</u> its <u>volume</u>.
>
> So the <u>hippo</u> has a <u>smaller</u> surface area compared to its volume.

3) The <u>smaller</u> its <u>surface area</u> compared to its <u>volume</u>, the <u>harder</u> it is
   for an organism to <u>exchange substances</u> with its environment.

Multicellular Organisms Need Exchange Surfaces

1) <u>Single-celled organisms</u> have a <u>large surface area</u> compared to their <u>volume</u>.

2) So, they can <u>exchange all the substances</u> they need across their <u>surface</u> (the <u>cell membrane</u>).

3) <u>Multicellular organisms</u> (such as <u>animals</u>) have a <u>smaller surface area</u> compared to their <u>volume</u>.

4) They <u>can't</u> normally exchange <u>enough substances</u> across their <u>outside surface</u> alone.

5) Instead, multicellular organisms have <u>specialised exchange surfaces</u>
   — see the next page and page 37 for some examples.

6) They also have <u>transport systems</u> that <u>carry</u> substances <u>to and from</u> their exchange surfaces.

7) The exchange surfaces are <u>ADAPTED</u> to allow <u>enough</u> of different substances to pass through:

> - They have a <u>thin membrane</u> (so substances only have a <u>short distance</u> to <u>diffuse</u>).
> - They have a <u>large surface area</u> (so <u>lots</u> of a substance can <u>diffuse</u> at once).
> - Exchange surfaces in <u>animals</u> have <u>lots of blood vessels</u>
>   (so stuff can get into and out of the blood <u>quickly</u>).
> - <u>Gas exchange surfaces</u> in animals (e.g. alveoli) are <u>ventilated</u> too — air moves in and out.

Surface area to volume ratios crop up a lot in biology...

...so try to learn about them now. Remember that, generally, a <u>smaller</u> object has a <u>larger</u> surface area to volume ratio than a bigger object, which is useful if substances are being exchanged across the surface.

More on Exchanging Substances

Here are a couple of examples of exchange surfaces inside your body...

Gas Exchange Happens in the Lungs

1) Oxygen (O_2) and carbon dioxide (CO_2) are exchanged in the lungs.

2) The lungs contain millions of little air sacs called alveoli. This is where gas exchange happens.

3) The alveoli are specialised for the diffusion of oxygen and carbon dioxide. They have:
   - A large surface area.
   - Very thin walls (so gases don't have far to diffuse).
   - A good blood supply.

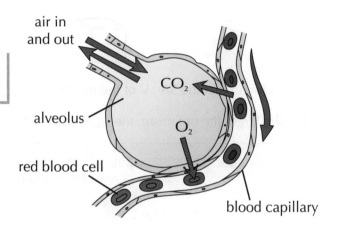

air in and out

CO_2

alveolus

O_2

red blood cell

blood capillary

The Villi Provide a Really Big Surface Area

1) The inside of the small intestine is covered in millions of villi.

2) They increase the surface area so that digested food is absorbed more quickly into the blood.

3) They have:
   - a single layer of surface cells,
   - a very good blood supply.

The digested food moves into the blood by diffusion and by active transport (see page 33).

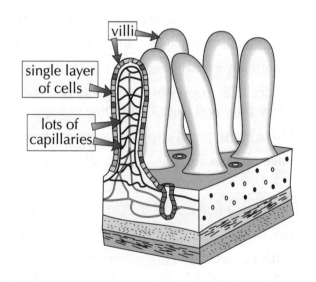

villi

single layer of cells

lots of capillaries

Humans need alveoli for gas exchange

You might get asked to explain how the adaptations of the alveoli help gas exchange, or how the small intestine is adapted for absorbing food. So, make sure you know what those adaptations are and why they increase the rate of exchange. There are some more structures coming up on the next page...

More on Exchanging Substances

More stuff on exchange surfaces for diffusion now — only this time they're in <u>plants</u> and <u>fish</u>.

The **Structure of Leaves** Lets Gases **Diffuse** In and Out of Cells

1) Plant leaves need to <u>take in carbon dioxide</u> for photosynthesis, and <u>get rid</u> of <u>oxygen</u> and <u>water vapour</u>.

2) The underneath of the leaf is an <u>exchange surface</u>. It's covered in small <u>holes</u> called <u>stomata</u>.

3) <u>Carbon dioxide diffuses</u> through the stomata <u>into</u> the leaf.

4) <u>Oxygen</u> and <u>water vapour</u> diffuse <u>out</u> through the stomata.

5) The size of the stomata are controlled by <u>guard cells</u> — see page 69.

6) The <u>flattened shape</u> of the leaf increases the <u>area</u> of its exchange surface.

7) The <u>walls of the cells</u> inside the leaf are another exchange surface. Gases diffuse <u>into</u> and <u>out of</u> the cells through these walls.

8) There are <u>air spaces</u> inside the leaf to <u>increase</u> the <u>area</u> of these surfaces.

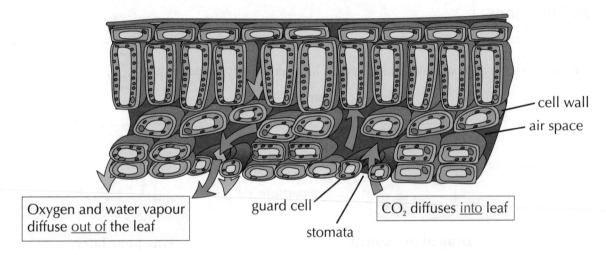

cell wall
air space

Oxygen and water vapour diffuse <u>out of</u> the leaf

guard cell

stomata

CO_2 diffuses <u>into</u> leaf

Gills Have a **Large Surface Area** for **Gas Exchange**

1) The <u>gills</u> are the <u>gas exchange surface</u> in <u>fish</u>.

2) Water (containing <u>oxygen</u>) flows into the fish's <u>mouth</u> and passes out through the <u>gills</u>.

3) In the gills, <u>oxygen</u> diffuses from the <u>water</u> into the <u>blood</u>. Carbon dioxide diffuses from the <u>blood</u> into the <u>water</u>.

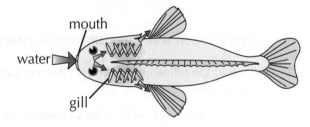

mouth

water

gill

4) The gills are made up of lots of <u>thin plates</u>. This gives them a <u>large surface area</u> for <u>gases</u> to be <u>exchanged</u>.

5) The plates have lots of <u>blood capillaries</u>. So they have a <u>good blood supply</u> to <u>speed up diffusion</u>.

6) They also have a <u>thin layer</u> of surface cells. So the gases only have to diffuse a <u>short distance</u>.

Exchange surfaces make diffusion quick and easy

Multicellular organisms are really <u>well adapted</u> for getting the substances they need to their cells. It makes sense — if they couldn't do this well, they'd die out. A <u>large surface area</u> is a key way that organisms' exchange surfaces are made more effective — molecules can only diffuse through a membrane when they're right next to it, and a large surface area means that <u>a lot more molecules</u> are close to the membrane.

Warm-Up & Exam Questions

Question time again — Warm-Up first, then Exam (or the other way round if you want to be different).

Warm-Up Questions

1) What is the word for the spreading out of particles from an area of higher concentration to an area of lower concentration?
2) True or false? Larger objects usually have smaller surface area to volume ratios than smaller objects.
3) How do villi in the small intestine help food to be absorbed more quickly?
4) Name one other exchange surface in humans.
5) What is the name of the small holes for exchanging gases on the underside a leaf?
6) Give one way in which the structure of a gill is adapted for effective gas exchange.

Exam Questions

1   **Figure 1** shows a cup of water which has just had a drop of dye added to it.   *Grade 3-4*

Figure 1

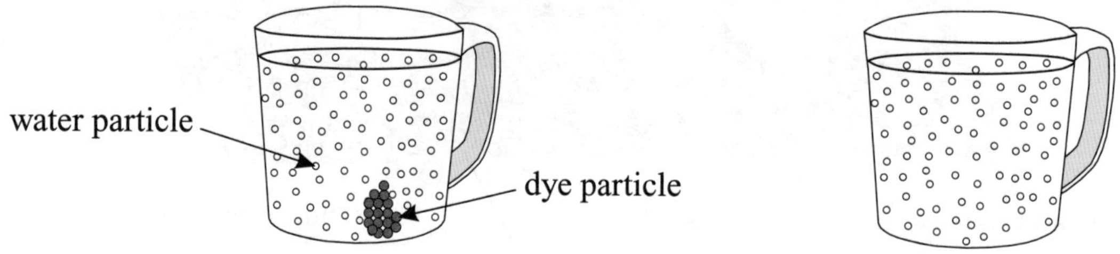

water particle

dye particle

Drop of dye added   **One hour later**

1.1   Complete **Figure 1** by drawing the molecules of dye in the cup after one hour.

[1 mark]

1.2   Describe the effect that a higher temperature would have on diffusion.

[1 mark]

2   Active transport is an important form of transport in organisms.   *Grade 3-4*

2.1   Which of the following is a correct description of active transport?
Tick **one** box.

☐ The movement of substances from an area of higher concentration to an area of lower concentration, without requiring energy.

☐ The movement of substances from an area of lower concentration to an area of higher concentration, without requiring energy.

☐ The movement of substances from an area of higher concentration to an area of lower concentration, requiring energy.

☐ The movement of substances from an area of lower concentration to an area of higher concentration, requiring energy.

[1 mark]

Exam Questions

2.2 Which of the following processes involve active transport?
Tick **two** boxes.

☐ Movement of mineral ions from the soil into root hair cells

☐ Movement of carbon dioxide from the air into the stomata of leaves

☐ Movement of oxygen from the water into the blood of fish

☐ Movement of nutrients, such as glucose, from the gut into the blood

[2 marks]

3 **Figure 2** shows a tank divided in two by the structure labelled **X**. *Grade 3-4*
Osmosis will occur between the two sides of the tank.

Figure 2

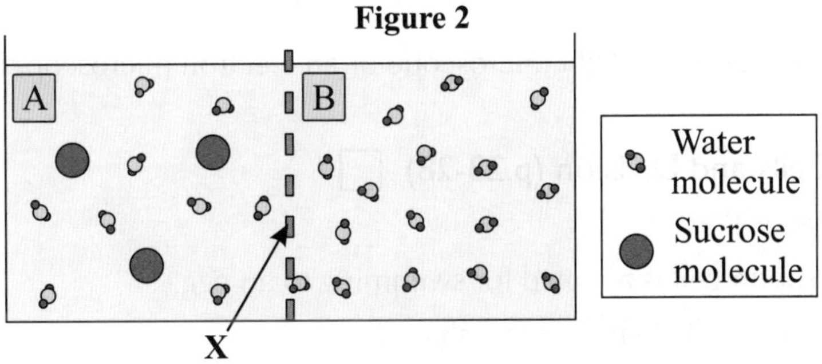

3.1 Name the structure labelled **X** on **Figure 2**.

[1 mark]

3.2 Which of the following will happen to the level of liquid on side **B**? Tick **one** box.

☐ The liquid level on side B will remain the same.

☐ The liquid level on side B will fall.

☐ The liquid level on side B will rise.

[1 mark]

PRACTICAL

4 In an experiment, four 50 mm long cylinders were cut from a fresh potato. *Grade 4-5*
The cylinders were then placed in different sugar solutions.
After 24 hours the potato cylinders were removed and measured. The results are shown in **Table 1**.

Table 1

Cylinder	1	2	3	4
Length after 24 hours (mm)	40	43	51	55
Change in length (mm)				+5

4.1 Complete **Table 1** by calculating the change in length for cylinders 1-3.

[1 mark]

4.2 Explain the change that occurred to the length of cylinder 4.

[2 marks]

Revision Summary for Topic 1

Well, that's <u>Topic 1</u> done and dusted. Now there's only one way to find out whether you've learnt anything from it. And you know what that is, I'll bet. It's obvious... I mean, there's a whole load of questions staring you in the face — chances are, it's got to involve those in some way. And sure enough, it does.

- Try these questions and <u>tick off each one</u> when you <u>get it right</u>.
- When you've done <u>all the questions</u> under a heading and are <u>completely happy</u> with it, tick it off.

Cells and Microscopy (p.17-21) ☑

1) What type of cells are bacteria — prokaryotic or eukaryotic? ☑
2) Name five subcellular structures that both plant and animal cells have. ☑
3) What three things do plant cells have that animal cells don't? ☑
4) Where is the genetic material found in:
   a) animal cells,
   b) bacterial cells? ☑
5) Which has a higher resolution — a light microscope or an electron microscope? ☑

Differentiation, Stem Cells and Division (p.23-28) ☑

6) What is cell differentiation? ☑
7) Give two ways that a sperm cell is adapted for swimming to an egg. ☑
8) Draw a diagram of a nerve cell. Why is it this shape? ☑
9) Give one way that embryonic stem cells could be used to cure diseases. ☑
10) Why might some people be against using human embryos in stem cell research? ☑
11) What are chromosomes? ☑
12) What is the cell cycle? ☑
13) What do multicellular organisms use mitosis for? ☑

Exchanging Substances (p.30-37) ☑

14) What is diffusion? ☑
15) How is the rate of diffusion affected by concentration? ☑
16) What type of molecules move by osmosis? ☑
17) Name the process that plants use to take up mineral ions from the soil. ☑
18) Give three ways that exchange surfaces can be adapted for diffusion. ☑
19) Give one way in which alveoli are adapted for gas exchange. ☑
20) Give two ways that the villi in the small intestine are adapted for absorbing digested food. ☑
21) Name the holes in the surface of a leaf that gases diffuse through. ☑

Cell Organisation

Some organisms are made of <u>lots</u> of cells. To get a <u>working</u> organism, these cells need to be <u>organised</u>.

Large Multicellular Organisms are Made Up of Organ Systems

1) <u>Cells</u> are the <u>basic building blocks</u> that make up <u>all living organisms</u>.
2) <u>Specialised cells</u> carry out a <u>particular function</u> (see p.23-24).
3) These specialised cells form <u>tissues</u>, which form <u>organs</u>, which form <u>organ systems</u> (see below).
4) <u>Large multicellular organisms</u> (e.g. humans) have different <u>systems</u> inside them for <u>exchanging</u> and <u>transporting</u> materials.

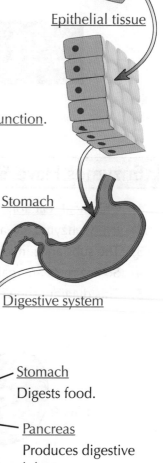

Epithelial cell

Similar Cells Make Up Tissues

1) A <u>tissue</u> is a <u>group</u> of <u>similar cells</u> that work together to carry out a <u>function</u>.
2) E.g. <u>epithelial tissue</u> is a type of tissue made of <u>epithelial cells</u>. It <u>covers</u> some parts of the human body, e.g. the <u>inside</u> of the <u>gut</u>.

Epithelial tissue

Tissues Make Up Organs

1) An <u>organ</u> is a group of <u>different tissues</u> that work together to perform a certain <u>function</u>.
2) For example, the <u>stomach</u> is an organ. <u>Epithelial tissue</u> lines the inside and outside of the stomach.

Stomach

Organs Make Up Organ Systems

1) An <u>organ system</u> is a <u>group of organs</u> working together to perform a <u>function</u>.
2) The <u>digestive system</u> is an organ system found in humans and other mammals.
3) It <u>breaks down</u> and <u>absorbs</u> food.
4) It's made up of these organs:

Digestive system

Salivary glands
Produce digestive juices.

You need to know where these organs are on a diagram.

Liver
Produces bile.

Large intestine
Absorbs water from undigested food, leaving faeces (poo).

Stomach
Digests food.

Pancreas
Produces digestive juices.

Small intestine
Digests food and absorbs soluble food molecules, e.g. glucose.

5) Organ systems work together to make entire <u>organisms</u>.

Remember — cells, tissues, organs, organ systems

OK, so from this page you should know that <u>cells</u> are organised into <u>tissues</u>, the tissues into <u>organs</u>, the organs into <u>organ systems</u> and the organ systems into a whole <u>organism</u>.

Enzymes

Chemical reactions are what make you work. And enzymes are what make them work.

Enzymes Are Catalysts

1) Living things have tons of reactions going on inside their cells.

2) These reactions are controlled by enzymes.

Enzymes are important in metabolism — see page 96.

3) Enzymes are large proteins.

4) They speed up reactions inside living things by acting as catalysts:

A CATALYST is a substance which INCREASES the speed of a reaction,
without being CHANGED or USED UP in the reaction.

Enzymes Have Special Shapes

1) Chemical reactions usually involve things either being split apart or joined together.
2) Every enzyme has an active site with a unique shape.
3) The substance involved in the reaction has to fit into the active site for the enzyme to work.
4) So enzymes are really picky — they usually only catalyse one specific reaction.
5) This diagram shows the 'lock and key' model of enzyme action:

The substance that an enzyme acts on is called the substrate.

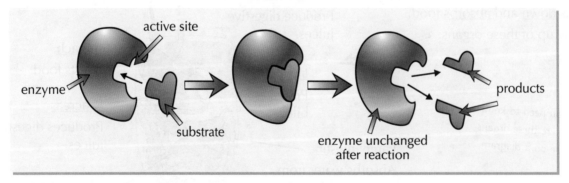

This is a useful model but it's a bit simpler than how enzymes actually work.

Enzymes speed up chemical reactions

Just like you've got to have the correct key for a lock, you've got to have the right substrate for an enzyme.
As you can see in the diagram above, if the substrate doesn't fit, the enzyme won't catalyse the reaction...

Enzymes

Enzymes are clearly very clever, but they need just the right <u>conditions</u> if they're going to work properly.

Enzymes Need the Right Temperature...

1) <u>Temperature</u> affects the <u>rate</u> of a reaction involving an enzyme.
2) A higher temperature <u>increases</u> the rate at first.
3) But if it gets <u>too hot</u>, some of the <u>bonds</u> holding the enzyme together <u>break</u>.
4) This changes the shape of the enzyme's <u>active site</u>, so the substrate <u>won't fit</u> any more — the enzyme is <u>denatured</u>.
5) All enzymes have a <u>temperature</u> that they work best at — their <u>optimum</u> temperature.

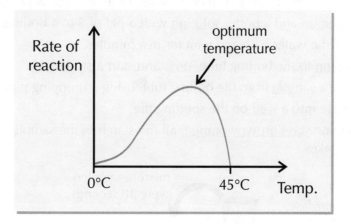

... and the Right pH

1) <u>pH</u> can affect the rate of a reaction involving an enzyme.
2) If the pH is <u>too high</u> or <u>too low</u>, it affects the <u>bonds</u> holding the enzyme together.
3) This changes the <u>shape</u> of the <u>active site</u>, and <u>denatures</u> the enzyme.
4) All enzymes have a <u>pH</u> that they work best at — their <u>optimum</u> pH.

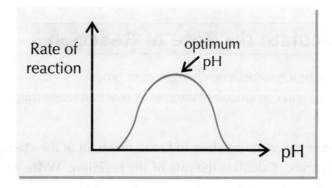

Most enzymes catalyse just one reaction

The <u>optimum temperature</u> for most human enzymes is around <u>normal body temperature</u>.
And <u>stomach enzymes</u> work best at <u>low pH</u>, but the enzymes in your <u>small intestine</u> like a <u>higher pH</u>.

Investigating Enzymatic Reactions

Give this page a read and you'll soon know how to investigate the effect of pH on the rate of enzyme activity.

You Can **Investigate** the Effect of **pH** on **Enzyme Activity**

> 1) The enzyme amylase catalyses the breakdown of starch to sugar.
> 2) You can detect starch using iodine solution — if starch is present, the iodine solution will change from browny-orange to blue-black.

1) Put a drop of iodine solution into every well of a spotting tile.
2) Set up a water bath at 35 °C.
(You could use a Bunsen burner and a beaker of water, or an electric water bath.)
3) Add some amylase solution and a buffer solution with a pH of 5 to a boiling tube.
4) Put the boiling tube in the water bath and wait for five minutes.
5) Add some starch solution to the boiling tube, mix, and start a stop clock.
6) Every 30 seconds, take a sample from the boiling tube using a dropping pipette.
7) Put a drop of the sample into a well on the spotting tile.
8) When the iodine solution stays browny-orange, all the starch in the sample has been broken down. Record how long this takes.

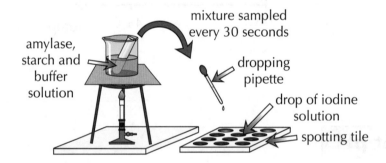

9) Repeat the experiment with buffer solutions of different pH values.
10) As the pH changes, the time it takes for the starch to be broken down should also change.
11) Remember to control any variables each time you repeat the experiment. This will make it a fair test. For example, the concentration and volume of the amylase solution should always be the same.

Here's How to **Calculate** the **Rate of Reaction**

1) Rate is a measure of how much something changes over time.
2) For the experiment above, you can calculate the rate of reaction using this formula:

$$\text{Rate} = \frac{1000}{\text{time}}$$

The time taken for amylase to break down all of the starch in a solution was 90 seconds. Calculate the rate of the reaction. Write your answer in s^{-1}.

Rate of reaction = 1000 ÷ time = 1000 ÷ 90 s
= 11 s^{-1}

s^{-1} just means 'per second'.

You can investigate other factors too...

You could easily adapt this experiment to investigate how factors other than pH affect the rate of amylase activity. For example, you could use a water bath to investigate the effect of temperature.

Enzymes and Digestion

The <u>enzymes</u> used in <u>digestion</u> are produced by <u>cells</u>. They're released into the <u>gut</u> to mix with food.

Digestive Enzymes Break Down Big Molecules

1) <u>Starch</u>, <u>proteins</u> and <u>fats</u> are BIG molecules.
2) They're <u>too big</u> to pass through the walls of the digestive system.
3) So <u>digestive enzymes</u> break these BIG molecules down into smaller ones.
4) These smaller, <u>soluble</u> molecules can <u>easily</u> be <u>absorbed</u> into the <u>bloodstream</u>.

Carbohydrases

- <u>Amylase</u> is an example of a <u>carbohydrase</u>.
- Amylase is made in the <u>salivary glands</u>, <u>pancreas</u> and <u>small intestine</u>.
- It works in the <u>mouth</u> and <u>small intestine</u>.

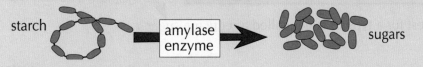

Starch is a carbohydrate.

Proteases

- Proteases are made in the <u>stomach</u>, <u>pancreas</u> and <u>small intestine</u>.
- They work in the <u>stomach</u> and <u>small intestine</u>.

Lipases

- Lipases are made in the <u>pancreas</u> and <u>small intestine</u>.
- They work in the <u>small intestine</u>.

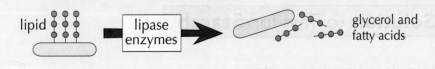

Lipids are fats and oils.

5) The <u>products</u> of digestion can be used to make <u>new carbohydrates</u>, <u>proteins</u> and <u>lipids</u>.
6) <u>Glucose</u> is a <u>sugar</u> produced by digestion. Some of it is used in <u>respiration</u> (see p.93-94).

Bile Neutralises the Stomach Acid and Emulsifies Fats

1) Bile is <u>produced</u> in the <u>liver</u>. It's <u>stored</u> in the <u>gall bladder</u> before it's released into the <u>small intestine</u>.
2) Bile is <u>alkaline</u>. It <u>neutralises</u> hydrochloric acid (from the stomach) and makes conditions <u>alkaline</u>.
3) The enzymes in the small intestine <u>work best</u> in these alkaline conditions.
4) Bile also <u>emulsifies</u> fats. Emulsify means that it breaks the fats down into <u>tiny droplets</u>.
   This gives a <u>bigger surface area</u> of fat for lipase to work on. This makes its digestion <u>faster</u>.

 **PRACTICAL** # Food Tests

There are some clever ways to <u>identify</u> what type of <u>food molecule</u> a sample contains.

Prepare Your Food Sample First

For each test, you need to prepare a <u>food sample</u>. It's the same each time though — here's what you'd do:

1) Get a piece of food and <u>break it up</u> using a <u>pestle and mortar</u>.
2) Transfer the ground up food to a <u>beaker</u> and add some <u>distilled water</u>.
3) Give the mixture a good <u>stir</u> with a glass rod to <u>dissolve</u> some of the food.
4) <u>Filter</u> the solution using a <u>funnel</u> lined with <u>filter paper</u>. This will <u>get rid</u> of the <u>solid</u> bits of food.

Use the Benedict's Test to Test for Sugars

Glucose is a reducing sugar.

The <u>Benedict's test</u> is used to test for a type of sugar called a <u>reducing sugar</u>. Here's how you do it:

1) Prepare a <u>food sample</u> and transfer $5 \ cm^3$ to a test tube.

2) Prepare a <u>water bath</u> so that it's set to <u>75 °C</u>.

3) Add some <u>Benedict's solution</u> to the test tube (about <u>10 drops</u>) using a pipette.

4) Place the test tube in the water bath using a test tube holder. Leave it in there for <u>5 minutes</u>.

5) If the food sample contains a reducing sugar, the solution in the test tube will change from the normal <u>blue</u> colour to <u>green</u>, <u>yellow</u> or <u>brick-red</u>. The colour change depends on <u>how much</u> sugar is in the food.

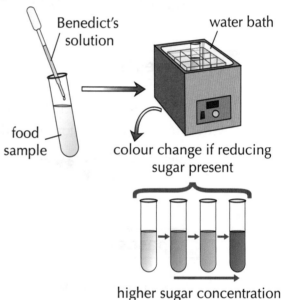

Benedict's solution

water bath

food sample

colour change if reducing sugar present

higher sugar concentration

Use Iodine Solution to Test for Starch

1) Make a <u>food sample</u> and transfer $5 \ cm^3$ to a test tube.

2) Add a few drops of <u>iodine solution</u>. <u>Gently shake</u> the tube to mix the contents.

3) If the sample contains <u>starch</u>, the colour of the solution will change from <u>browny-orange</u> to <u>black</u> or <u>blue-black</u>.

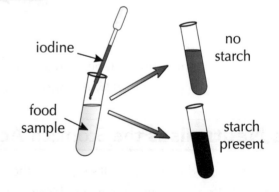

iodine

food sample

no starch

starch present

There are four food molecules you should know how to test for

You're halfway through them now. Turn the page to read about the other two — <u>proteins</u> and <u>lipids</u>...

Food Tests

There are a couple more <u>food tests</u> coming up on this page — for proteins and for lipids. As with the other tests, you need to use the method on the previous page to prepare a <u>sample</u> of your food first.

Use the **Biuret Test** to Test for **Proteins**

1) Prepare a <u>sample</u> of your food and transfer <u>2 cm³</u> to a test tube.

2) Add 2 cm³ of <u>biuret solution</u> to the sample. Mix the contents of the tube by <u>gently shaking</u> it.

3) If the food sample contains <u>protein</u>, the solution will change from <u>blue</u> to <u>purple</u>.

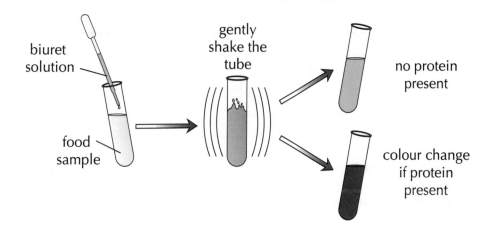

biuret solution

food sample

gently shake the tube

no protein present

colour change if protein present

Use the **Sudan III Test** to Test for **Lipids**

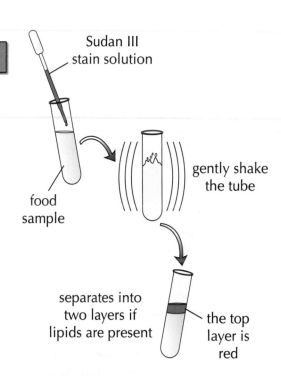

Sudan III stain solution

food sample

gently shake the tube

separates into two layers if lipids are present

the top layer is red

1) Prepare a <u>food sample</u> using the method on the previous page but <u>don't</u> filter it. Transfer <u>5 cm³</u> to a test tube.

2) Add <u>3 drops</u> of <u>Sudan III stain solution</u> to the test tube. <u>Gently shake</u> the tube.

3) If the sample contains <u>lipids</u>, the mixture will separate out into <u>two layers</u>. The top layer will be <u>bright red</u>.

PRACTICAL TIP

Make sure you think about all of the hazards...

<u>Iodine</u> is an <u>irritant</u> to the <u>eyes</u>, and the chemicals in the <u>biuret solution</u> are <u>dangerous</u>, so wear <u>safety goggles</u> for food tests. If you <u>spill</u> any of the chemicals on your <u>skin</u>, wash it off <u>straight away</u>. Be careful around the <u>water bath</u> in the <u>Benedict's test</u>, too. And if that's not enough to be cautious about, <u>Sudan III stain solution</u> is <u>flammable</u>, so keep it away from any <u>lit Bunsen burners</u>.

Warm-Up & Exam Questions

Doing well in exams isn't just about remembering all the facts, although that's important. You have to get used to the way the exam questions are phrased and make sure you always read them carefully.

Warm-Up Questions

1) Is the stomach a tissue or an organ?
2) What is the name for the part of an enzyme that a substrate fits into?
3) Which enzyme digests starch?
4) What are the products when lipids are broken down?
5) True or false? Protease enzymes are made in the liver.
6) Describe how you would prepare a food sample before testing it for the presence of different food molecules.

Exam Questions

1 **Figure 1** shows the human digestive system. (Grade 1-3)

1.1 Which label, **A-D**, shows the place where bile is produced?

[1 mark]

1.2 Use words from the box to complete the sentences below.

acidic	alkaline	neutral
lipids	starch	proteins

Bile makes conditions in the small intestine ....

Bile also emulsifies ....

[2 marks]

2 **Figure 2** shows the effect of temperature on the action of an enzyme. (Grade 3-4)

2.1 At what temperature does the enzyme work best?

[1 mark]

2.2 What name is given to the temperature at which an enzyme works best?

[1 mark]

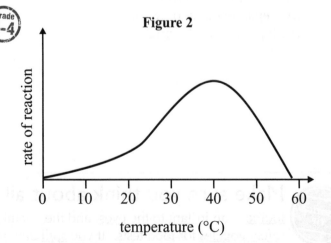

Figure 2

Exam Questions

3   **Figure 3** represents the action of an enzyme in catalysing a biological reaction.

3.1   In terms of the enzyme's shape, explain why
an enzyme only catalyses one reaction.

[1 mark]

Figure 3

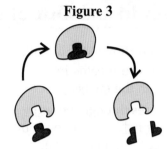

3.2   The optimum pH of the enzyme is pH 7.
Explain what effect a very low pH would
have on the activity of the enzyme.

[2 marks]

PRACTICAL

4   A student wanted to know which substances were present in a food sample. She prepared
a solution containing the food, and added some of the solution to each of three test tubes.
She then added different chemicals to each test tube, to test for different food molecules.
Her results are shown in **Table 1**.

Table 1

Test tube	Chemical added to test tube	Description of solution in test tube
A	Iodine	Blue-black
B		Blue
C	Sudan III stain solution	In two layers. Top layer red.

4.1   Complete the table to show what solution would have been added to test tube **B** to test for proteins.

[1 mark]

4.2   Does the food sample contain starch? Explain your answer.

[1 mark]

4.3   Does the food sample contain lipids? Explain your answer.

[1 mark]

PRACTICAL

5   A student was investigating the effect of pH on the rate of amylase activity.
He used a syringe to put amylase solution and a buffer solution with a pH of 6
into a boiling tube. He then used a different syringe to add a starch solution to
the boiling tube. He mixed the contents and then started a stop clock.

5.1   Suggest why he used two different syringes when adding substances to the boiling tube.

[1 mark]

Every 30 seconds the student took a sample from the boiling tube and
tested it for the presence of starch. When there was no starch present
he stopped the stop clock. He repeated the experiment three times.

5.2   The average time taken for the starch in the boiling tube to be broken down was 60 seconds.
Calculate the rate of the reaction.
Give your answer in s^{-1} to 2 significant figures. Use the formula: $rate = \dfrac{1000}{time}$

[2 marks]

The Lungs

You need <u>oxygen</u> to supply your <u>cells</u> for <u>respiration</u> (see p.93-94). You also need to get rid of <u>carbon dioxide</u>. This all happens in your <u>lungs</u> when you breathe air in and out.

Air Moves In and Out of the Lungs

1) This diagram shows the <u>structure</u> of the lungs:
2) The air that you breathe in goes through the <u>trachea</u>.
3) Then it passes through the <u>bronchi</u>, then the <u>bronchioles</u> and ends up in the <u>alveoli</u> (small air sacs).

One bronchus, two bronchi.
One alveolus, many alveoli.

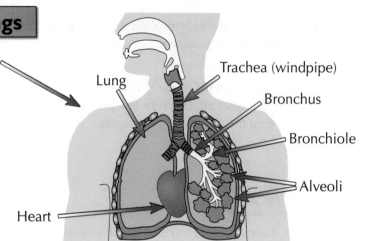

Lung
Trachea (windpipe)
Bronchus
Bronchiole
Alveoli
Heart

Alveoli Carry Out Gas Exchange

1) <u>Alveoli</u> in the lungs are surrounded by <u>blood capillaries</u>.
2) <u>Blood</u> comes <u>into</u> the lungs through the capillaries. It contains <u>lots</u> of <u>carbon dioxide</u> and <u>very little oxygen</u>.
3) <u>Oxygen</u> diffuses (see p.30) <u>out</u> of the <u>air</u> in the alveolus (where there's a <u>higher</u> concentration) <u>into</u> the <u>blood</u> (where there's a <u>lower</u> concentration).
4) <u>Carbon dioxide</u> diffuses <u>out</u> of the <u>blood</u> (higher concentration) <u>into</u> the <u>air</u> in the alveolus (lower concentration).
5) The blood then leaves the lungs and travels around the <u>body</u>.

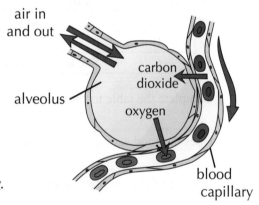

air in and out
carbon dioxide
alveolus
oxygen
blood capillary

You Can Calculate the Breathing Rate

<u>Breathing rate</u> is how <u>fast</u> a person moves air in and out of their lungs. Here's how to calculate it:

 **EXAMPLE:**

Bob takes 91 breaths in 7 minutes. Calculate his average breathing rate in breaths per minute.

breaths per minute = number of breaths ÷ number of minutes

= 91 ÷ 7

= 13 breaths per minute

REVISION TIP

Take a deep breath...

...and make sure you get to grips with the layout of the innards of your chest. Try sketching the diagram and adding the labels until you think you've got it sussed. If you know where the <u>trachea</u>, <u>bronchi</u>, <u>bronchioles</u> and <u>alveoli</u> are, then you're making a pretty good start.

Circulatory System — The Heart

The circulatory system carries <u>food</u> and <u>oxygen</u> to every cell in the body.
It also carries <u>waste products</u> to where they can be removed from the body.

Humans Have a **DOUBLE** Circulatory System

The circulatory system is made up of the <u>heart</u>, <u>blood vessels</u> and <u>blood</u>.
A <u>double circulatory system</u> is <u>two circuits</u> joined together:

1) In the first circuit, the <u>heart</u> pumps <u>deoxygenated</u> blood (blood <u>without oxygen</u>) to the <u>lungs</u>. The blood picks up oxygen in the lungs.

2) <u>Oxygenated</u> blood (blood <u>with oxygen</u>) then <u>returns</u> to the heart.

3) In the second circuit, the <u>heart</u> pumps <u>oxygenated</u> blood around all the <u>other organs</u> of the <u>body</u>. This delivers oxygen to the body cells.

4) <u>Deoxygenated</u> blood <u>returns</u> to the heart to be pumped out to the <u>lungs</u> again.

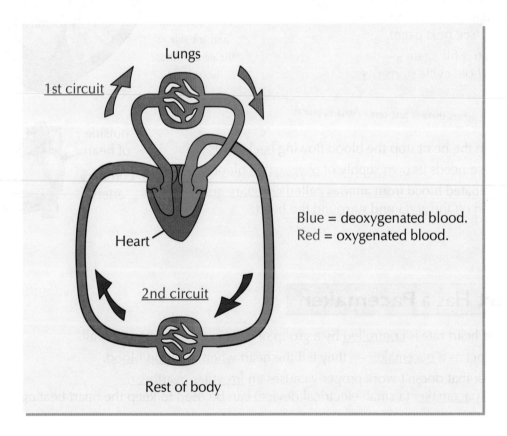

Blue = deoxygenated blood.
Red = oxygenated blood.

First, blood goes to the lungs to pick up oxygen...

...then it takes the oxygen around the rest of the body to all of the cells. The next few pages are also about the circulatory system, so make sure you understand what a <u>double circulatory system</u> is before moving on.

Circulatory System — The Heart

Now you know how the circulatory system works <u>overall</u>, it's time to look at the individual <u>parts</u> of it. First up, the <u>heart</u>...

The **Heart Pumps Blood** Around The Body

1) The <u>heart</u> is an organ with <u>four chambers</u>. The walls of the chambers are mostly made of <u>muscle tissue</u>.
2) This muscle tissue is used to <u>pump blood</u> around the body. Here's how:

> 1) <u>Blood flows into</u> the two <u>atria</u> from the <u>vena cava</u> and the <u>pulmonary vein</u>.
> 2) The <u>atria pump</u> the blood into the <u>ventricles</u>.
> 3) The <u>ventricles</u> pump the blood <u>out</u> of the heart:
>   • Blood from the <u>right ventricle</u> goes through the <u>pulmonary artery</u> to the <u>lungs</u>.
>   • Blood from the <u>left ventricle</u> goes through the <u>aorta</u> to the rest of the <u>body</u>.
> 4) The blood then flows to the <u>organs</u> through <u>arteries</u>, and <u>returns</u> through <u>veins</u> (see next page).
> 5) The atria fill again — the whole cycle <u>starts over</u>.

Atrium is when there is just one. Atria is plural.

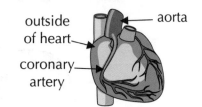

3) The <u>valves</u> in the heart stop the blood flowing <u>backwards</u>.
4) The heart also needs its <u>own</u> supply of <u>oxygenated</u> blood.
5) It gets oxygenated blood from arteries called <u>coronary arteries</u>. These branch off the <u>aorta</u> and <u>surround</u> the heart.

The **Heart** Has a **Pacemaker**

1) Your resting heart rate is <u>controlled</u> by a group of cells in the <u>right atrium</u> wall.
2) These cells act as a <u>pacemaker</u> — they tell the heart <u>when</u> to <u>pump blood</u>.
3) A pacemaker that doesn't work properly causes an <u>irregular heartbeat</u>. An <u>artificial pacemaker</u> (a small electrical device) can be used to keep the heart beating <u>regularly</u>.

Make sure you know the names of the parts of the heart

The heart diagram on this page is really important. Try copying it out a few times to get yourself really familiar with it. If you get your <u>atria</u> and <u>ventricles</u> mixed up, think about how the shape of the heart comes to a point at the bottom, just like a letter V, which is where the <u>ventricles</u> are.

Circulatory System — Blood Vessels

Blood needs a good set of 'tubes' to carry it round the body. Here's a page on the different types:

Arteries Carry Blood Under Pressure

1) Arteries carry blood <u>away</u> from the heart.
2) The heart pumps the blood out at <u>high pressure</u>.
3) So artery walls are <u>strong</u> and <u>elastic</u>.
4) They have thick layers of <u>muscle</u> to make them <u>strong</u>.
5) They also have <u>elastic fibres</u> to allow them to <u>stretch</u> and <u>spring back</u>.
6) The walls are <u>thick</u> compared to the size of the hole down the middle (the "<u>lumen</u>").

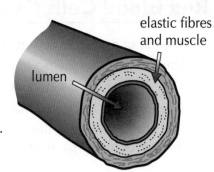
elastic fibres and muscle
lumen

Capillaries are Really Small

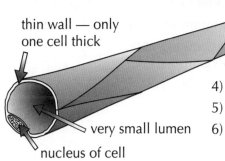
thin wall — only one cell thick
very small lumen
nucleus of cell

1) Arteries branch into <u>capillaries</u>.
2) Capillaries are really <u>tiny</u> — too small to see.
3) They carry the blood <u>really close</u> to <u>every cell</u> in the body to <u>exchange substances</u> with them.
4) They have <u>gaps</u> in their walls, so substances can <u>diffuse</u> in and out.
5) They supply <u>food</u> and <u>oxygen</u>, and take away <u>waste</u> like CO_2.
6) Their walls are usually <u>only one cell thick</u>. This means that diffusion is <u>very fast</u> because there is only a <u>short distance</u> for molecules to travel.

Veins Take Blood Back to the Heart

1) Capillaries <u>join up</u> to form <u>veins</u>.
2) The blood is at <u>lower pressure</u> in the veins. This means the walls don't need to be as <u>thick</u> as artery walls.
3) Veins have a <u>bigger lumen</u> than arteries. This helps the blood <u>flow</u> despite the lower pressure.
4) They also have <u>valves</u>. These help keep the blood flowing in the <u>right direction</u>.

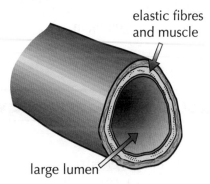
elastic fibres and muscle
large lumen

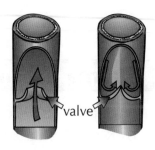
valve

You Can Calculate the Rate of Blood Flow

The <u>rate of blood flow</u> is the amount of blood that passes through a blood vessel in a given <u>time</u>. Here's how to <u>calculate</u> it:

EXAMPLE: **1300 ml of blood passed through an artery in 4 minutes.**
Calculate the rate of blood flow through the artery in ml per minute.

rate of blood flow = volume of blood ÷ number of minutes
= 1300 ÷ 4
= 325 ml per minute

Circulatory System — Blood

Blood is a tissue (see p.41). One of its jobs is to act as a huge transport system. It has four main parts...

Red Blood Cells Carry Oxygen

1) The job of red blood cells is to carry oxygen from the lungs to all the cells in the body.
2) Their shape gives them a large surface area for absorbing oxygen.
3) They contain a red substance called haemoglobin.
4) Haemoglobin is the stuff that allows red blood cells to carry oxygen.
5) Red blood cells don't have a nucleus —
   this leaves more space for carrying oxygen.

White Blood Cells Defend Against Infection

1) White blood cells are part of your immune system — see page 80.
2) Some can change shape to gobble up unwelcome microorganisms.
3) Others produce molecules called antibodies and antitoxins to defend against microorganisms.
4) Unlike red blood cells, they do have a nucleus.

Platelets Help Blood Clot

1) These are small fragments of cells. They have no nucleus.
2) They help the blood to clot (clump together) at a wound.
3) This stops all your blood pouring out.
4) It also stops any microorganisms getting in.

Plasma is the Liquid That Carries Everything in Blood

This is a pale straw-coloured liquid. It carries:
1) Red and white blood cells and platelets.
2) Food molecules (like glucose and amino acids).
3) Waste products (like carbon dioxide and urea).
4) Hormones.
5) Proteins.

Blood — red blood cells, white blood cells, platelets and plasma

Sometimes, when you're ill, you might have a sample of your blood taken so that it can be analysed. Blood tests can be used to diagnose loads of things — not just disorders of the blood. This is because the blood transports so many chemicals produced by so many organs... and it's easy to take a sample of blood.

Warm-Up & Exam Questions

There are some nice diagrams to learn on the previous few pages. If you don't bother, you'll feel pretty silly if you turn over the exam paper and the first question asks you to label a diagram of the heart. Just saying... Anyway, let's see if these questions get your blood pumping...

Warm-Up Questions

1) What is the name of the tubes that the trachea splits into?
2) What is the function of the coronary arteries?
3) What does an artificial pacemaker do?
4) What do veins do?
5) True or false? Red blood cells don't have a nucleus.

Exam Questions

1 **Figure 1** shows the human heart and four blood vessels, as seen from the front. The left ventricle and the right atrium have been labelled.

Figure 1

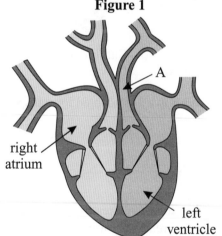

right atrium

A

left ventricle

1.1 Name the part labelled **A**.

[1 mark]

1.2 What is the function of the left ventricle? Tick **one** box.

☐ It pumps blood to the lungs.

☐ It pumps blood around the body.

☐ It prevents the backflow of blood.

[1 mark]

1.3 Complete the sentence.

Deoxygenated blood enters the right atrium through the ....

[1 mark]

Exam Questions

2   Draw **one** line from each part of the blood to its function.   (Grade 1-3)

            part of blood   **function**

| red blood cell | | carrying everything in the blood |

| plasma | | carrying oxygen |

| platelets | | helping the blood to clot |

[2 marks]

3   The cell shown in **Figure 2** transports oxygen around the body.   (Grade 3-4)

Figure 2

View from above   Cut through view

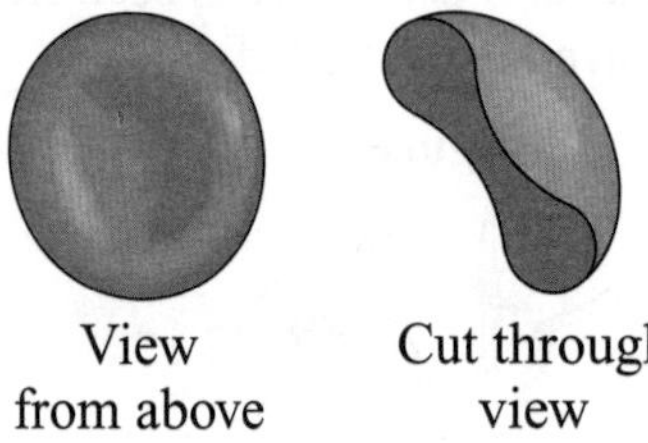

Explain how the shape of the cell in **Figure 2** is adapted for transporting oxygen.

[1 mark]

4   A student ran for 12 minutes.   (Grade 4-5)

4.1   During this 12 minute run, the student took 492 breaths.
Calculate his average breathing rate in breaths per minute.

[1 mark]

4.2   The student also measured his heart rate before and during his run.
Before his run, the student's heart rate was at its natural resting rate.
Outline how natural resting heart rate is controlled.

[1 mark]

5   Blood cells are carried in the bloodstream inside blood vessels.   (Grade 4-5)

5.1*   Capillaries are one type of blood vessel.
Explain how the structure of a capillary allows it to carry out its function.

[4 marks]

5.2   Blood flows through different types of blood vessels at different rates.
The volume of blood that passed through an artery in 2.5 minutes was 1.155 litres.
Calculate the rate of blood flow through the artery in ml/min.

[2 marks]

Cardiovascular Disease

Cardiovascular diseases are diseases of the heart or blood vessels. One example is coronary heart disease.

Coronary Heart Disease is a Disease of the Coronary Arteries

1) The coronary arteries supply the heart muscle with blood.
2) Coronary heart disease is when layers of fatty material (called fatty deposits) build up in the coronary arteries. This causes the arteries to become narrow.
3) This reduces the blood flow to the heart muscle.
4) This means less oxygen can get to the heart muscle. This can result in a heart attack.

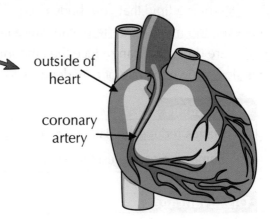

outside of heart

coronary artery

Stents Keep Coronary Arteries Open

1) Stents are tubes that are put inside coronary arteries by surgery. They keep the arteries open.
2) This allows blood to reach the heart muscles and reduces the risk of a heart attack.

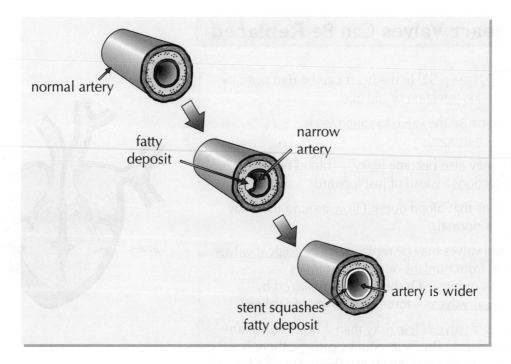

normal artery

fatty deposit

narrow artery

stent squashes fatty deposit

artery is wider

3) Stents are effective for a long time. Recovery time from the surgery is also quite quick.
4) But there are risks. These include having a heart attack during the operation, or getting an infection after surgery. Patients may also develop a blood clot near the stent.

Coronary heart disease is a type of cardiovascular disease

Coronary heart disease is caused by the arteries being blocked by fatty material — if the heart muscle can't get enough oxygen, then it can't work properly. And if the heart can't work properly, well, you're in trouble.

Cardiovascular Disease

You've read about stents, so now it's time for a second treatment for coronary heart disease — statins.

Statins Reduce Cholesterol in the Blood

1) Cholesterol is a lipid that your body needs.
2) However, too much cholesterol can cause fatty deposits to form inside arteries.
3) Statins are drugs that can reduce the amount of cholesterol in the blood.
4) This slows down the rate of fatty deposits forming.

Advantages

1) Statins reduce the risk of strokes, coronary heart disease and heart attacks.
2) Some studies suggest that statins may also help prevent some other diseases.

Disadvantages

1) Statins must be taken regularly over a long time. A person could forget to take them.
2) Statins can cause unwanted side effects, for example, headaches.
3) The effect of statins isn't instant. It takes time for their effect to work.

Faulty Heart Valves Can Be Replaced

1) The valves (see p.52) in the heart can be damaged by heart attacks, infection or old age.

2) This may cause the valve to stiffen, so it won't open properly.

3) A valve may also become leaky — blood flows in both directions instead of just forward.

4) This means that blood doesn't flow around the body as well as normal.

5) Damaged valves may be replaced by biological valves — valves from humans or other mammals (e.g. cows or pigs). Or they can be replaced by mechanical valves — these are man-made valves.

6) Replacing a valve is less risky than a heart transplant (see next page). But as it requires surgery, there is a risk of bleeding and infection. There can also be problems with blood clots.

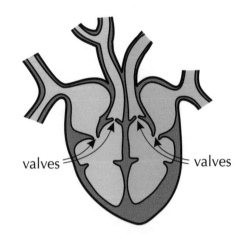

valves — valves

There are risks with any treatment for cardiovascular disease

Anything involving surgery on the heart is going to be risky, but even taking statins comes with a risk of side effects. Doctors and patients have to weigh up the benefits against the risks.

More on Cardiovascular Disease

One final page on cardiovascular disease. Having the valves replaced isn't the only surgery for cardiovascular disease — when someone has heart failure, surgeons can <u>replace</u> the <u>whole heart</u>.

An **Artificial Heart** Can **Pump Blood** Round the Body

1) A <u>heart transplant</u> is when a person's heart is <u>replaced</u> by a <u>donor heart</u> (a heart from someone who has recently died).

2) This can happen if someone has <u>heart failure</u>. <u>Heart failure</u> is when the heart <u>can't pump</u> enough <u>blood</u>.

3) The <u>lungs</u> may also be replaced if they are <u>diseased</u>.

4) If a donor heart <u>isn't available</u>, doctors may fit an <u>artificial heart</u> (a <u>machine</u> that pumps blood around the body).

5) Artificial hearts can be used to keep a person <u>alive</u> until a donor heart is <u>available</u>. Or they can help a person <u>recover</u> by allowing the heart to <u>rest</u> and <u>heal</u>.

6) Sometimes artificial hearts are <u>permanent</u>, so a donor heart isn't needed anymore.

7) Here are some of the <u>advantages</u> and <u>disadvantages</u> of artificial hearts:

Advantage

Artificial hearts are made from <u>metals</u> or <u>plastics</u>. This makes them <u>less likely</u> to be <u>attacked</u> by the body's immune system (see page 80) than a donor heart.

Disadvantages

1) <u>Surgery</u> to fit an artificial heart can lead to <u>bleeding</u> and <u>infection</u>. (This can also happen with transplant surgery.)

2) Artificial hearts <u>don't</u> work as well as healthy <u>natural</u> ones.

Some of the disadvantages of an artificial heart are advantages of a donor heart.

3) Blood doesn't flow through artificial hearts as <u>smoothly</u> as through a natural heart. This can cause <u>blood clots</u> and lead to <u>strokes</u>.

4) The patient has to take <u>drugs</u> to <u>thin</u> their blood. This means they can <u>bleed</u> a lot more than is usual if they have an accident.

Don't lose heart...

You could be asked to <u>evaluate</u> treatments for <u>cardiovascular disease</u>. Don't panic — just use any information you're given and your own knowledge to weigh up the <u>advantages</u> and <u>disadvantages</u>. Make sure your answer doesn't just focus on <u>one side</u> — e.g. don't just talk about the advantages and ignore the disadvantages. You should also include a <u>conclusion</u> that you can <u>back up</u>.

Warm-Up & Exam Questions

Hopefully I've persuaded you by now that it's a good idea to try these questions. Believe me, when you're sitting with your real exam paper in front of you, you'll feel so much better knowing that you've already been through loads of practice questions. So off you go...

Warm-Up Questions

1) Which vessels are affected in coronary heart disease?
2) If someone has heart failure, and there is no donor heart available, how might they be treated?
3) What is an artificial heart?

Exam Questions

1   There are different ways to treat coronary heart disease.

1.1   Complete **Table 1** to give the names of the treatments described.

Table 1

Description of treatment	Name of treatment
Tubes that are put inside arteries to keep them open	
Drugs that reduce cholesterol in the blood	

[2 marks]

1.2   Suggest **one** disadvantage to a patient of taking drugs to reduce blood cholesterol.

[1 mark]

2   A patient is taken into hospital. They are diagnosed as having a leaky heart valve. The doctor decides that a surgeon should replace the valve.

2.1   Give the **two** types of valve that the surgeon might use.

[2 marks]

2.2   Suggest **one** risk of replacing the faulty valve.

[1 mark]

3   **Figure 1** shows a cross-section of a blood vessel in someone with coronary heart disease.

3.1   Name the substance labelled **X** on **Figure 1**.

[1 mark]

3.2   Explain how the presence of this substance can affect oxygen delivery to the heart muscle.

[2 marks]

Figure 1

Health and Disease

Try as we might, it's unlikely that we'll be in tip-top condition for all of our lives — <u>disease</u> tends to get us all at some point. There are lots of <u>different types</u> of diseases we could get...

Diseases are a Major Cause of Ill Health

1) <u>Health</u> is the <u>state</u> of <u>physical</u> and <u>mental wellbeing</u>.

2) This means that both the <u>body</u> and <u>mind</u> are <u>well</u>.

3) Diseases are often responsible for causing <u>ill health</u>.

4) Diseases can be <u>communicable</u> or <u>non-communicable</u>:

Communicable diseases are sometimes called infectious diseases.

Communicable Diseases

1) These are diseases that can <u>spread</u> from <u>person to person</u> or between <u>animals</u> and <u>people</u>.
2) Communicable diseases can be caused by <u>bacteria</u>, <u>viruses</u>, <u>parasites</u> or <u>fungi</u>.
3) <u>Measles</u> and <u>malaria</u> are examples of communicable diseases. See pages 75-78 for more.

Non-Communicable Diseases

1) These are diseases that <u>cannot spread</u> between people or between animals and people.
2) <u>Coronary heart disease</u> (see page 57) is an example of a non-communicable disease.

Different Types of Disease Can Interact

Sometimes a disease can cause <u>other</u> physical and mental health issues. Here are a few examples:

1) The <u>immune system</u> helps to fight off <u>pathogens</u> (see page 80). Some people have <u>problems</u> with their immune system. This makes them <u>more likely</u> to <u>suffer</u> from communicable diseases.
   Pathogen is just the fancy term for a microorganism that can cause disease.
2) An <u>immune system reaction</u> (caused by a pathogen) may lead to an <u>allergic</u> reaction, such as a <u>skin rash</u>. Or it may worsen the symptoms of <u>asthma</u> for asthma sufferers.
3) <u>Viruses</u> infect <u>cells</u> in the body. This can lead to some types of <u>cancer</u>.
4) <u>Physical</u> health problems may also lead to <u>mental</u> health problems. For example, a person may become <u>depressed</u> if they can't carry out <u>everyday activities</u> because of <u>ill health</u>.

Communicable diseases can spread...

...but <u>non-communicable</u> diseases <u>can't</u>. Remember that — it's really important.

Health and Disease

Ill health isn't just about having a disease — there are plenty of other causes.
And then there's the cost of ill health to consider too — there might be more to it than you'd first thought...

Other Factors Can Also Affect Your Health

There are plenty of factors other than diseases that can also affect your health. For example:

1) A poor diet can affect your physical and mental health. A good diet is balanced and provides your body with everything it needs, in the right amounts.

2) Being constantly under lots of stress can lead to poor health.

3) Your life situation can affect your health. This is because it affects how easily you can access medicine or things that prevent you from getting ill. E.g. being able to buy condoms to prevent the spread of some sexually transmitted diseases.

Non-Communicable Diseases Can Be Costly

The Human Cost

1) Tens of millions of people around the world die from non-communicable diseases every year.
2) People with these diseases may have a lower quality of life or a shorter lifespan — this is the human cost.

The Financial Cost

1) The financial cost of researching and treating these diseases is huge.
2) It can also be expensive for individuals if they have to move or adapt their home because of a disease. If a person has to give up work or if they die, then their family's income will be reduced.
3) A reduction in the number of people able to work can also affect a country's economy.

Lots of things affect health, and ill health can be costly

A human cost is the effect something has on humans. A financial cost is to do with how much spending something results in. When you're studying biology, you'll come across lots of things that have a human cost or a financial cost (or both). Some things can have quite far-reaching knock-on effects.

Risk Factors for Non-Communicable Diseases

You've probably heard the term '<u>risk factor</u>' before. These next couple of pages have lots of info on them. There's nothing too tricky, but there's quite a bit to read — take it slowly and make sure it goes in.

Risk Factors Increase Your Chance of Getting a Disease

1) Risk factors are things that are linked to an <u>increased chance</u> of getting a certain disease.

2) However, risk factors <u>don't mean</u> that someone <u>will</u> definitely get the disease.

3) They can be:
   - part of a person's <u>lifestyle</u> (for example, how much exercise they do),
   - substances in a person's <u>environment</u> (e.g. air pollution),
   - substances in a person's <u>body</u> (e.g. asbestos fibres in the lungs can cause cancer).

4) Many <u>non-communicable</u> diseases are caused by <u>several</u> risk factors that <u>interact</u> with each other.

5) Lifestyle factors can have different effects <u>locally</u>, <u>nationally</u> and <u>globally</u>.
   - <u>Globally</u>, non-communicable diseases are <u>more common</u> in developed countries. This is because people in developed countries generally <u>earn more</u> and can buy <u>high-fat</u> food.
   - <u>Nationally</u>, cardiovascular disease, obesity and Type 2 diabetes are more common in <u>poorer</u> areas. This is because people in <u>poorer areas</u> are <u>more likely</u> to smoke, have a poor diet and not exercise.
   - Your <u>individual choices</u> affect how common a disease is <u>locally</u>.

Some Risk Factors Can Cause a Disease Directly

Some risk factors are able to <u>directly cause</u> a disease. For example:

> Smoking can cause <u>cardiovascular disease</u>, <u>lung disease</u> and <u>lung cancer</u>. It damages the <u>walls</u> of <u>arteries</u> and the <u>lining</u> of the <u>lungs</u>.

Lifestyle can have a big impact on a person's health
Smoking makes a person <u>more likely</u> to get certain diseases. The next page has some more risk factors.

Risk Factors for Non-Communicable Diseases

Here are a few more risk factors that can directly cause disease:

Obesity may cause Type 2 diabetes by making the body less sensitive or resistant to (not affected by) insulin.

There's more about Type 2 diabetes on page 108.

Drinking too much alcohol can damage the brain and the liver.

Smoking and drinking alcohol when pregnant can cause health problems for the unborn baby.

Cancer can be caused by exposure to certain substances or radiation. Things that cause cancer are known as carcinogens. Ionising radiation (e.g. from X-rays) is an example of a carcinogen.

There's more about cancer coming up on the next page.

Risk Factors Can be Identified Using Correlation

Some risk factors don't directly cause a disease.
BUT there is a correlation between the risk factor and the disease.

See page 14 for more about correlations.

For example, a lack of exercise and a high fat diet are risk factors for cardiovascular disease, but they can't cause the disease. It's the resulting high cholesterol levels (see p.58) that can cause it.

It's hard to avoid all risk factors of disease...

...but remember that risk factors that cause disease don't mean you'll definitely get the disease. They just increase the chance of it happening. Also, remember that not all risk factors cause disease. Many are just correlated with the disease, meaning there is a relationship between them.

Cancer

The more we understand <u>cancer</u>, the better our chances of <u>avoiding</u> and <u>beating</u> it.

Cancer is Caused by **Uncontrolled Cell Growth and Division**

1) Changes in cells can lead to <u>uncontrolled</u> growth and division. This results in a <u>tumour</u> (a mass of cells).
2) Tumours can be <u>benign</u> or <u>malignant</u>:

<table>
<tr>
<td>

1) <u>Benign</u> tumours are masses of <u>abnormal cells</u>.
2) They stay in <u>one place</u> (usually within a membrane).
3) They don't <u>invade</u> other parts of the body.
4) This type <u>isn't</u> normally dangerous, and the tumour <u>isn't</u> cancerous.

</td>
<td>

1) <u>Malignant</u> tumours spread to other parts of the body.
2) The cells can <u>break off</u> and travel in the <u>bloodstream</u>.
3) The cells <u>get into</u> healthy tissues and form <u>secondary tumours</u>.
4) Malignant tumours are <u>dangerous</u> and can be fatal — <u>they are cancers</u>.

</td>
</tr>
</table>

Risk Factors Can **Increase** the **Chance** of **Some Cancers**

Scientists have identified <u>lots</u> of risk factors for cancers. For example:

Lifestyle Factors

1) <u>Smoking</u> — Smoking is linked to <u>many types</u> of cancer.
2) <u>Obesity</u> — Obesity has also been linked to <u>many different cancers</u>.
3) <u>Viral infection</u> — Infection with some viruses can <u>increase</u> the chances of developing <u>certain types</u> of cancer.
4) <u>UV exposure</u> — The Sun produces <u>UV radiation</u>. This radiation has been linked to an increased chance of developing skin cancer.

Genetic Factors

1) Genes are passed on (<u>inherited</u>) from <u>parent</u> to <u>offspring</u> — see page 116.
2) Sometimes you can <u>inherit faulty genes</u> that make you <u>more likely</u> to get cancer.

People are Now **More Likely** to **Survive Cancer**

People have become <u>more likely</u> to <u>survive</u> cancer because:

1) <u>Treatments</u> have improved.
2) Doctors can diagnose cancer <u>earlier</u>.
3) More people are being <u>screened</u> (tested) for cancer.
4) People know more about the <u>risk factors</u> for cancer.

Knowing about the risk factors can help to protect people

E.g. people are now more aware that wearing <u>sun block</u> reduces the risk of skin cancer from UV radiation.

Warm-Up & Exam Questions

It's time for some more questions — don't just assume that you've remembered everything you just read on the past few pages. Give these a go, and then go back over anything that you struggled with.

Warm-Up Questions

1) True or false? Health is the state of physical wellbeing only.
2) What does it mean if a disease is 'communicable'?
3) True or false? Physical health problems may lead to mental health problems.
4) What disease can uncontrolled cell division lead to?

Exam Questions

1   Diseases can be communicable or non-communicable. **Grade 1-3**
     What is meant by a non-communicable disease?
     Tick **one** box.

☐   A disease that can be spread between people or between animals and people.

☐   A disease that cannot be spread between people or between animals and people.

☐   A disease cause by uncontrolled cell growth and division.

☐   A disease caused by the build-up of fatty material in the coronary arteries.

[1 mark]

2   Tumours can be either benign or malignant. **Grade 3-4**

Complete **Table 1** to show whether each statement is true for benign tumours, malignant tumours, or both.
Put **one or two** ticks in each row.

Table 1

	Benign	Malignant
The tumour is made up of a mass of cells formed by uncontrollable division and growth.		
The tumour cells can break off and travel into the bloodstream.		
The tumour is cancerous.		

[3 marks]

3   Many diseases have risk factors. **Grade 4-5**

3.1   What is meant by the term 'risk factor'?

[1 mark]

3.2   Give **one** risk factor for lung disease.

[1 mark]

3.3   Name **one** carcinogen that is a risk factor for cancer.

[1 mark]

Plant Cell Organisation

Just like in animals, plant cells are also organised. Here are a few examples of plant <u>tissues</u> and <u>organs</u>.

Plant Cells Are Organised Into Tissues And Organs

1) Plants are made of <u>organs</u>. These organs <u>work together</u> to make <u>organ systems</u>.

2) For example, <u>stems</u>, <u>roots</u> and <u>leaves</u> are all plant organs.
They work together to <u>transport</u> (carry) substances around the plant.

3) Plant <u>organs</u> are made of <u>tissues</u>. Examples of plant tissues are:

For more on photosynthesis, see page 87.

- <u>Epidermal tissue</u> — this <u>covers</u> the whole plant.
- <u>Palisade mesophyll tissue</u> — this is the part of the leaf where most <u>photosynthesis</u> happens.
- <u>Spongy mesophyll tissue</u> — this is the part of the leaf that has big <u>air spaces</u>.
This allows <u>gases</u> to <u>diffuse</u> in and out of cells.
- <u>Xylem</u> and <u>phloem</u> — these transport things like <u>water</u>, <u>mineral ions</u> and <u>food</u>
around the roots, stems and leaves (see next page).
- <u>Meristem tissue</u> — this is found at the <u>growing tips</u> of <u>shoots</u> and <u>roots</u>.

Leaves Contain Epidermal, Mesophyll, Xylem and Phloem Tissue

1) The leaf is where <u>photosynthesis</u> and <u>gas exchange</u> happens in a plant.

2) The <u>structures</u> of the tissues in a leaf are <u>related</u> to their <u>function</u>:

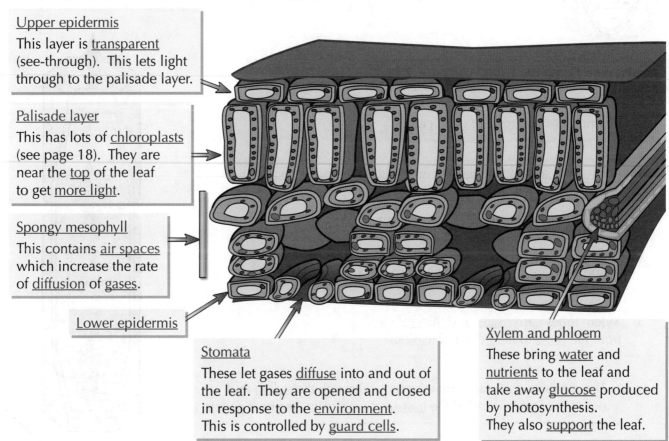

<u>Upper epidermis</u>
This layer is <u>transparent</u> (see-through). This lets light through to the palisade layer.

<u>Palisade layer</u>
This has lots of <u>chloroplasts</u> (see page 18). They are near the <u>top</u> of the leaf to get <u>more light</u>.

<u>Spongy mesophyll</u>
This contains <u>air spaces</u> which increase the rate of <u>diffusion</u> of <u>gases</u>.

<u>Lower epidermis</u>

<u>Stomata</u>
These let gases <u>diffuse</u> into and out of the leaf. They are opened and closed in response to the <u>environment</u>.
This is controlled by <u>guard cells</u>.

<u>Xylem and phloem</u>
These bring <u>water</u> and <u>nutrients</u> to the leaf and take away <u>glucose</u> produced by photosynthesis.
They also <u>support</u> the leaf.

Each tissue in a leaf is adapted for its function

There are a lot of weird names here, so make sure you spend plenty of time on this page.
Try <u>drawing</u> your own leaf diagram. <u>Label</u> it with the different tissues and <u>describe</u> each type.

Transpiration and Translocation

Flowering plants have <u>two</u> separate types of vessel — <u>xylem</u> and <u>phloem</u> — for transporting stuff around. <u>Both</u> types of vessel go to <u>every part</u> of the plant, but they are totally <u>separate</u>.

Phloem Tubes Transport Food

Food (mainly dissolved sugars)

1) Phloem tubes are made of <u>elongated</u> (stretched out) <u>living cells</u>.

2) There are <u>end walls</u> between the cells. These have <u>pores</u> (small holes) to allow <u>cell sap</u> to flow through.

3) Plants make <u>food substances</u> (e.g. dissolved <u>sugars</u>) in their <u>leaves</u>.

4) Phloem tubes transport these <u>food substances</u> around the plant for <u>immediate use</u> or for <u>storage</u>.

Cell sap is a liquid that's made up of the substances being transported and water.

5) The transport goes in <u>both directions</u>.

6) This process is called <u>translocation</u>.

Xylem Tubes Take Water Up

Water and minerals

1) Xylem tubes are made of <u>dead cells</u>.

2) The cells are joined together with a <u>hole</u> down the <u>middle</u>.

3) There are no <u>end walls</u> between the cells.

4) The cells are <u>strengthened</u> with a material called <u>lignin</u>.

5) Xylem tubes carry <u>water</u> and <u>mineral ions</u> from the <u>roots</u> to the <u>stem</u> and <u>leaves</u>.

6) The movement of water from the <u>roots</u>, through the <u>xylem</u> and out of the <u>leaves</u> is called the <u>transpiration stream</u> (see next page).

REVISION TIP

Xylem vessels carry water, phloem vessels carry sugars

Make sure you don't get your phloem <u>mixed up</u> with your xylem. To help you to learn which is which, you could remember that phl<u>o</u>em transports substances in b<u>o</u>th directions, but xylem only transports things upwards — x<u>y</u> to the sk<u>y</u>. It might just bag you a mark or two on exam day...

Transpiration

If you don't water a house plant for a few days it starts to go all droopy. Plants need <u>water</u>.

Transpiration is the **Loss of Water** from the Plant

1) Transpiration is caused by <u>evaporation</u> and <u>diffusion</u> of water from a plant's surface (mainly the leaves).

2) Here's how it happens:

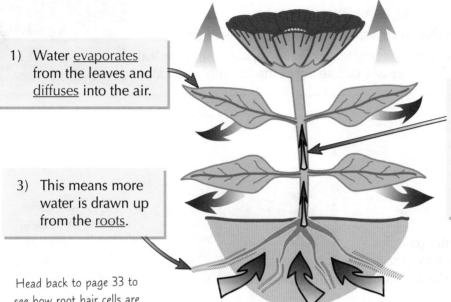

Evaporation is when water turns from a liquid into a gas. See page 30 for more on diffusion.

1) Water <u>evaporates</u> from the leaves and <u>diffuses</u> into the air.

2) This creates a slight <u>shortage</u> of water in the leaf. More water is drawn up from the rest of the plant through the <u>xylem tubes</u> to replace it.

3) This means more water is drawn up from the <u>roots</u>.

Head back to page 33 to see how root hair cells are adapted for taking up water.

3) There's a constant <u>stream of water</u> through the plant. This is called the <u>transpiration stream</u>.

Guard Cells Control **Gas Exchange** and **Water Loss**

guard cell

stoma
(plural — stomata)

1) Water is <u>lost</u> from a plant's leaves through the <u>stomata</u>.

2) Stomata are surrounded by <u>guard cells</u>.

3) These <u>change shape</u> to control the size of the stomata.

4) When the plant has <u>lots</u> of water the guard cells fill with it and get <u>fat</u>. This makes the stomata <u>open</u> so <u>gases</u> can be exchanged for <u>photosynthesis</u>.

5) When the plant is <u>short</u> of water, the guard cells lose water and become <u>floppy</u>. This makes the stomata <u>close</u>. This helps stop too much water vapour <u>escaping</u>.

6) There are usually <u>more</u> stomata on the <u>bottoms</u> of leaves than on the tops. This is because the <u>lower surface</u> is <u>cooler</u> — so <u>less water</u> gets <u>lost</u>.

Transpiration involves evaporation and diffusion

A big tree loses about a <u>thousand litres</u> of water from its leaves <u>every single day</u> — it's a fact.
That's as much water as the average person drinks in a whole year, so the <u>roots</u> have to be very effective at drawing in water from the soil. Which is why they have all those root <u>hairs</u>, you see.

The Rate of Transpiration

The rate of transpiration varies according to the environmental conditions...

Transpiration Rate is Affected by Four Main Things:

Air Flow

1) The more windy it is, the faster transpiration happens.
2) Fast moving air means that water vapour around the leaf is swept away.
3) This means there's a higher concentration of water vapour inside the leaf compared to outside. So water will diffuse out of the leaf more quickly.

Temperature

1) The warmer it is, the faster transpiration happens.
2) This is because the water particles have more energy. So they evaporate and diffuse out of the stomata faster.

Many factors affect transpiration rate by affecting the rate of diffusion of water. There's more about diffusion on page 30.

Humidity

1) If the air is humid there's a lot of water in it already.
2) This means there isn't much of a difference between the inside and the outside of the leaf.
3) This means that diffusion will not happen very fast.
4) The drier the air around a leaf, the faster transpiration happens.

Light Intensity

1) The brighter the light, the greater the transpiration rate.
2) Photosynthesis can't happen in the dark, so stomata begin to close as it gets darker.
3) When the stomata are closed, very little water can escape.

Transpiration is fastest when it's windy, warm, dry and bright

The weather can make a big difference to how quickly water is lost from the leaves of a plant. Make sure you know these four factors, and that you understand why they affect transpiration rates.

Warm-Up & Exam Questions

Just a few simple Warm-Up Questions and a few slightly harder Exam Questions stand between you and mastering cell organisation and transport in plants...

Warm-Up Questions

1) Where is meristem tissue found in a plant?
2) Which layer of plant tissue contains lots of chloroplasts?
3) True or false? Substances pass in both directions through xylem vessels.
4) State one of the main factors that affects the rate of transpiration in plants.

Exam Questions

1 Leaves contain many types of tissue. *Grade 3-4*

1.1 Which type of plant tissue contains air spaces for the diffusion of gases?
Tick **one** box.

☐ epidermal tissue

☐ xylem tissue

☐ spongy mesophyll tissue

[1 mark]

1.2 Which type of plant tissue forms the transparent layer covering the outside of plant?
Tick **one** box.

☐ epidermal tissue

☐ palisade mesophyll tissue

☐ spongy mesophyll tissue

[1 mark]

2 **Figure 1** shows a vessel that transports cell sap. *Grade 3-4*

Figure 1

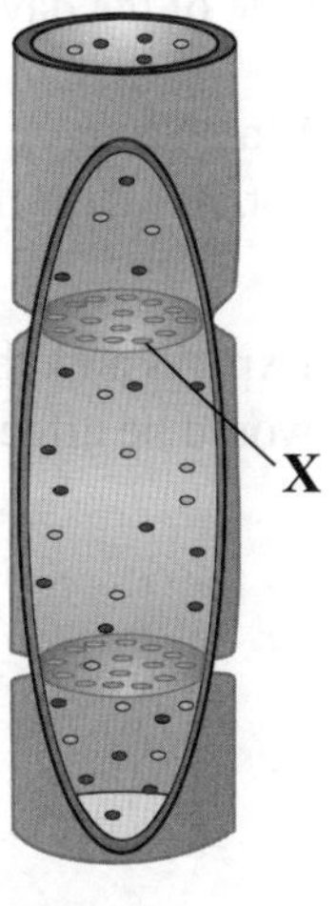

2.1 Name the type of vessel shown in **Figure 1**.

[1 mark]

2.2 Explain why the vessel has the pores labelled **X** on **Figure 1**.

[1 mark]

2.3 Name the movement of cell sap through the plant's transport vessels.

[1 mark]

Exam Questions

3 Stomata are found on the surface of leaves.

3.1 Complete the sentence below about stomata.

Stomata are opened and closed by cells called ....

[1 mark]

3.2 **Figure 2** shows a stoma in different conditions.

Figure 2

Condition **A**   Condition **B**

Which condition, **A** or **B**, shows a stoma when the plant is short of water? Explain your answer.

[1 mark]

4 Plants absorb water and mineral ions through their root hair cells.
Xylem vessels transport water and mineral ions from the roots of a plant to the leaves.

4.1 Describe the structure of xylem vessels.

[3 marks]

4.2 Name the process of water transport through a plant.

[1 mark]

5 The water loss from a plant during two different days is shown on the graph in **Figure 3**.
One of the days was hot and dry, and the other day was cold and wet.

5.1 Which line, **A** or **B**, shows water loss on the
hot, dry day? Explain your answer.

[1 mark]

5.2* Explain how the rate of water loss from a plant
would be affected by windy weather.

[4 marks]

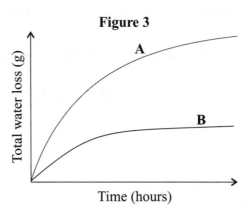

Figure 3

Revision Summary for Topic 2

Well, that's <u>Topic 2</u> finished. Now it's time to test how much you've taken in...
- Try these questions and <u>tick off each one</u> when you <u>get it right</u>.
- When you've done <u>all the questions</u> under a heading and are <u>completely happy</u> with it, tick it off.

Cell Organisation (p.41) ☑
1) What is a tissue?
2) Explain what is meant by the term 'organ system'.

The Role of Enzymes and Food Tests (p.42-47) ☑
3) Why can enzymes be described as catalysts?
4) What does it mean when an enzyme has been 'denatured'?
5) Describe how you could investigate the effect of pH on the rate of amylase activity.
6) List the three places where amylase is made in the human body.
7) What is the role of lipases?
8) Where is bile stored?
9) Name the solution that you would use to test for the presence of sugars in a food sample.

The Lungs and Circulatory System (p.50-54) ☑
10) Where does gas exchange happen in the lungs?
11) Name the four chambers of the heart.
12) Why does the heart have valves?
13) How are arteries adapted to carry blood away from the heart?
14) Which type of blood vessel is the smallest?
15) Why do red blood cells not have a nucleus?

Diseases and Risk Factors (p.57-65) ☑
16) Give two advantages and two disadvantages of statins.
17) What is the difference between biological and mechanical replacement heart valves?
18) Give an example of different types of disease interacting in the body.
19) What is a carcinogen?
20) Give two lifestyle factors that increase the chance of cancer.

Plant Cell Organisation and Transport (p.67-70) ☑
21) List the tissues that make up a leaf.
22) Explain how the structure of the palisade layer in a leaf is related to its function.
23) What is the function of phloem tubes?
24) What is transpiration?
25) List the four main things that affect transpiration.

Communicable Disease

If you're hoping I'll ease you gently into this new topic... no such luck. Straight on to the baddies of biology.

There Are **Several Types** of **Pathogen**

1) Pathogens are microorganisms that enter the body and cause disease.
2) They cause communicable (infectious) diseases.
3) Communicable diseases are diseases that can spread (see p.61).
4) Both plants and animals can be infected by pathogens.
5) There are four main types of pathogens:

> Bacteria   Viruses   Protists   Fungi

Pathogens Can Be **Spread** in **Different Ways**

Here are a few ways that pathogens can be spread:

Air
Pathogens can be carried in the air and can then be breathed in. Some pathogens are carried in the air in droplets made when you cough or sneeze.

Water
Some pathogens can be picked up by drinking or bathing in dirty water.

Direct Contact
Some pathogens can be picked up by touching surfaces they're on (e.g. the skin).

The **Spread** of Disease Can Be **Reduced** or **Prevented**

There are things that we can do to reduce or prevent the spread of disease, such as...

1) Being hygienic (clean) — For example, washing your hands before making food can stop you spreading pathogens onto the food and infecting a person who eats it.

2) Destroying vectors — Vectors are organisms that spread disease. Killing them helps to stop the disease from being passed on. Vectors that are insects can be killed using insecticides. Their habitats can also be destroyed so that they can't breed.

3) Isolating infected individuals — If you keep someone who has a communicable disease away from other people, it prevents them from passing it on to anyone else.

4) Vaccination (see page 82) — Vaccinations can stop people and animals from getting a communicable disease. This also stops them passing it on to others.

Bacterial Diseases

First up from the <u>pathogen</u> hall of fame are... <u>bacteria</u>.

Bacteria are Very Small **Living Cells**

1) Bacteria <u>reproduce rapidly</u> inside your body.
2) They can make you <u>feel ill</u> by <u>producing toxins</u> (poisons).
3) Toxins <u>damage</u> your <u>cells and tissues</u>.

Salmonella and Gonorrhea Are Two **Bacterial Diseases**

Salmonella

1) *Salmonella* is a type of <u>bacteria</u>. It causes <u>food poisoning</u>.

2) Infected people can suffer from <u>fever</u>, <u>stomach cramps</u>, <u>vomiting</u> and <u>diarrhoea</u>. These symptoms are caused by <u>toxins</u> from the bacteria.

3) You can get *Salmonella* food poisoning by:

- Eating <u>food</u> that's got *Salmonella* bacteria in it already, e.g. eating chicken that caught the disease whilst it was alive.
- Eating food that has been <u>made</u> where the bacteria is present, e.g. in an <u>unclean kitchen</u> or on the <u>hands</u> of the person making the food.

4) In the UK, most <u>poultry</u> (e.g. chickens and turkeys) are given a <u>vaccination</u> against *Salmonella*. This is to control the <u>spread</u> of the disease.

Gonorrhoea

1) Gonorrhoea is caused by <u>bacteria</u>.
2) <u>Gonorrhoea</u> is a <u>sexually transmitted disease</u> (STD).
3) STDs are passed on by <u>sexual contact</u>, e.g. having unprotected sex.
4) A person with gonorrhoea will get <u>pain</u> when they <u>urinate</u> (wee). Another symptom is a thick yellow or green <u>discharge</u> (fluid) from the <u>vagina</u> or the <u>penis</u>.
5) Gonorrhoea <u>used to be treated</u> with an <u>antibiotic</u> called <u>penicillin</u>. There are now <u>new strains</u> (types) of gonorrhoea that are <u>resistant</u> to (not killed by) penicillin. So this antibiotic <u>doesn't work</u> anymore.
6) To prevent the <u>spread</u> of gonorrhoea:

- People can be treated with <u>other antibiotics</u>,
- People should use <u>barrier methods</u> of contraception (see pages 112-113), such as <u>condoms</u>.

Viral Diseases

Viruses may be tiny but there are lots of diseases caused by them.

Viruses Are Not Cells — They're Much Smaller

1) Viruses reproduce rapidly inside your body.

2) They live inside your cells.

3) Inside your cells, they make lots of copies of themselves.

4) The cells will usually then burst, releasing all the new viruses.

5) This cell damage is what makes you feel ill.

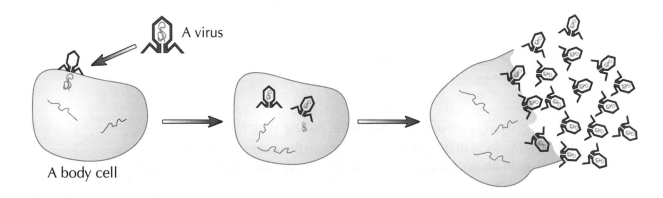

A virus

A body cell

Different Viruses Cause Different Diseases, Such as...

Measles

1) Measles is a viral disease. It is spread by droplets from an infected person's sneeze or cough.

2) People with measles develop a red skin rash.

3) They'll also show signs of a fever (a high temperature).

4) Measles can be very serious. People can die from measles if there are complications (problems).

5) Because of this, most people are vaccinated against measles when they're young.

Viral Diseases

HIV

1) <u>HIV</u> is a <u>virus</u> spread by <u>sexual contact</u> or by exchanging <u>bodily fluids</u> (e.g. blood). This can happen when people <u>share needles</u> when taking drugs.

2) To start with, HIV causes <u>flu-like symptoms</u> for a few weeks.

3) After that the person <u>doesn't</u> usually have any symptoms for several years.

4) HIV can be controlled with <u>antiretroviral drugs</u>. These stop the virus <u>copying itself</u> in the body.

5) If it's not controlled, the virus attacks the <u>immune cells</u> (see page 80).

6) If the body's immune system is badly damaged, it <u>can't cope</u> with <u>other infections</u> or <u>cancers</u>. At this stage, the virus is known as <u>late stage HIV infection</u> or <u>AIDS</u>.

Tobacco Mosaic Virus

1) <u>Tobacco mosaic virus</u> (<u>TMV</u>) is a <u>virus</u> that affects many species of <u>plants</u>, e.g. <u>tomatoes</u>.

2) It causes parts of the <u>leaves</u> to become <u>discoloured</u>. This gives them a <u>mosaic pattern</u>.

3) The discoloured leaves have <u>less chlorophyll</u> to absorb <u>light</u> (see p.87).

4) This means <u>less photosynthesis</u> happens in the leaves, so the plant can't make <u>enough food</u> to <u>grow</u>.

EXAM TIP

Don't be put off by something you haven't heard of...

If you're given some information about a disease you've <u>never heard of before</u>, don't panic. You just need to <u>use what you know</u> and <u>apply</u> it to the disease in the question. For example, if the disease is viral, just use what you know about viruses to answer the question.

Fungal and Protist Diseases

Sorry — I'm afraid there are some more <u>diseases</u> to learn about here...

Rose Black Spot is a Fungal Disease

1) <u>Rose black spot</u> is a disease caused by a <u>fungus</u>.

2) The fungus causes <u>purple or black spots</u> on the <u>leaves</u> of <u>rose plants</u>.
The leaves can then turn <u>yellow</u> and <u>drop off</u>.

3) This means that less <u>photosynthesis</u> can happen, so the plant doesn't <u>grow</u> very well.

4) It is spread in <u>water</u> or by the <u>wind</u>.

5) Gardeners can treat the disease using <u>fungicides</u> (chemicals that kill fungi).

6) They can also <u>strip</u> the <u>affected leaves</u> off the plant. These leaves then need to be <u>destroyed</u> so that the fungus can't spread to other rose plants.

Malaria is a Disease Caused by a Protist

1) <u>Malaria</u> is caused by a <u>protist</u>.

2) Part of the protist's <u>life cycle</u> takes place inside the mosquito.

3) The mosquitoes are <u>vectors</u>. They help <u>spread</u> malaria like this...

- The mosquitoes <u>pick up</u> the protist when they <u>feed</u> on an <u>infected animal</u>.
- The mosquitoes <u>don't</u> get malaria.
- They <u>pass on</u> the protist to other animals (like us) when they <u>bite</u> them.
- These animals <u>get malaria</u>.

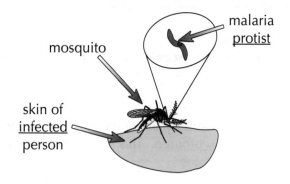

mosquito

malaria <u>protist</u>

skin of <u>infected</u> person

4) Malaria causes <u>repeating</u> episodes of <u>fever</u>. People can <u>die</u> from malaria.

5) The <u>spread</u> of malaria can be reduced by stopping the <u>mosquitoes</u> from <u>breeding</u>.

6) People can be protected from mosquito bites using <u>mosquito nets</u>.

REVISION TIP

Hang in there, this stuff is pretty gross, but it's nearly over...

Try drawing out a <u>table</u> with columns for 'disease', 'type of pathogen it's caused by', 'symptoms' and 'how it's spread', then fill it in for all the diseases on this page and the previous three. See how much you can write down <u>without</u> looking back at the page.

Warm-Up & Exam Questions

Have a go at these questions to test whether you know about each of the diseases covered on the previous pages, including their symptoms and how they are spread.

Warm-Up Questions

1) True or false? A communicable disease is a disease that can spread.
2) How is gonorrhoea passed between individuals?
3) Where do viruses live inside the human body?
4) What symptom of measles is shown on the skin?
5) Which disease causes the leaves of tomato plants to become discoloured?
6) What effect does rose black spot disease have on plants?

Exam Questions

1 Which of the following statements about malaria is **not** correct? Tick **one** box. *(Grade 1-3)*

☐ People with malaria can have repeating episodes of fever.

☐ Mosquitos are the vectors of malaria.

☐ Malaria is caused by a virus.

☐ People can be protected from mosquito bites by using mosquito nets.

[1 mark]

2 The spread of disease can be reduced or prevented in many ways. *(Grade 1-3)*

2.1 Which method is used to prevent the spread of *Salmonella* between people? Tick **one** box.

☐ hand-washing ☐ stopping vectors from breeding ☐ vaccinating people

[1 mark]

2.2 Which method is used to prevent the spread of measles between people? Tick **one** box.

☐ hand-washing ☐ stopping vectors from breeding ☐ vaccinating people

[1 mark]

3 Diseases are often recognised by their symptoms. *(Grade 3-4)*

3.1 Describe the first symptoms of HIV infection.

[1 mark]

3.2 Give **one** symptom of gonorrhoea.

[1 mark]

3.3 A person has food poisoning caused by *Salmonella*. Give **one** symptom that they may have.

[1 mark]

Fighting Disease

The human body has some pretty neat features when it comes to <u>fighting disease</u>.

Your Body Has a Pretty Good Defence System

The human body has got features that stop a lot of nasties getting inside. For example:

1) The <u>skin</u> — It <u>stops pathogens</u> getting <u>inside</u> you. It also <u>releases substances</u> that <u>kill pathogens</u>.

2) <u>Nose hairs</u> — They <u>trap</u> particles that could contain pathogens.

3) <u>Mucus (snot)</u> — The <u>trachea</u> and <u>bronchi</u> (airways — see page 50) release <u>mucus</u> to <u>trap</u> pathogens.

4) <u>Cilia</u> (hair-like structures) — The <u>trachea</u> and <u>bronchi</u> are lined with <u>cilia</u>. They <u>move</u> the <u>mucus</u> up to the back of the throat where it can be <u>swallowed</u>.

5) <u>Stomach acid</u> — The stomach makes <u>hydrochloric acid</u>. This <u>kills pathogens</u> in the stomach.

Your Immune System Can Attack Pathogens

1) If pathogens do make it into your body, your <u>immune system</u> kicks in to <u>destroy</u> them.
2) The most important part of your immune system is the <u>white blood cells</u>.
3) When they come across an invading pathogen they have <u>three lines of attack</u>:

Phagocytosis

White blood cells can <u>engulf</u> (surround) pathogens and <u>digest</u> them. This is called <u>phagocytosis</u>.

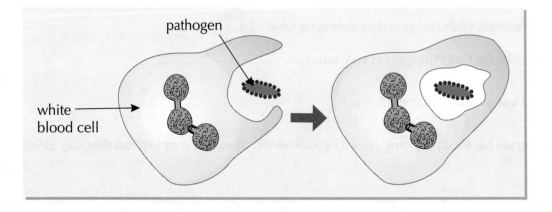

Fighting Disease

Producing **Antibodies**

1) Every invading pathogen has <u>unique molecules</u> on its surface. These molecules are called <u>antigens</u>.

2) When some types of white blood cell come across a <u>foreign antigen</u> (i.e. one they don't know), they will start to make <u>antibodies</u>.

3) Antibodies <u>lock onto</u> the invading pathogens. The antibodies made are <u>specific</u> to that type of antigen — they won't lock on to any others.

4) The antibodies make sure the pathogens can be <u>found</u> and <u>destroyed</u> by other white blood cells.

5) If the person is infected with the <u>same pathogen</u> again, the white blood cells will <u>rapidly</u> make the antibodies to kill it. This means the person is <u>naturally immune</u> to that pathogen and <u>won't get ill</u>.

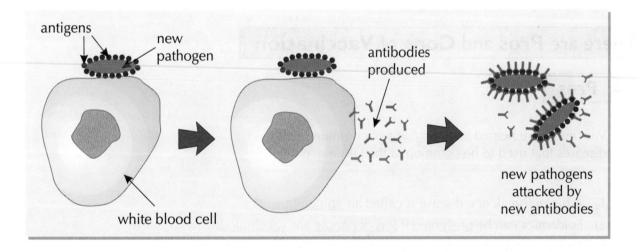

Producing **Antitoxins**

These <u>stop toxins</u> produced by the <u>invading bacteria</u> from working.

Fighting disease is one thing the body is really good at...

The <u>immune system</u> attacks pathogens that get <u>inside</u> the body. There are <u>three</u> ways that white blood cells <u>kill</u> pathogens — <u>phagocytosis</u>, making <u>antibodies</u> and making <u>antitoxins</u>. Make sure you know them <u>all</u>.

Fighting Disease — Vaccination

Vaccinations mean we don't always have to treat a disease — we can stop the disease in the first place.

Vaccination — Protects from Future Infections

1) Vaccinations involve injecting small amounts of dead or inactive pathogens into the body.
2) These pathogens have antigens on their surface.
3) The antigens cause your white blood cells to produce antibodies to attack the pathogens.
4) If you're infected with the same pathogen later, your white blood cells quickly produce lots of antibodies.
5) These antibodies kill the pathogen so you don't become ill.

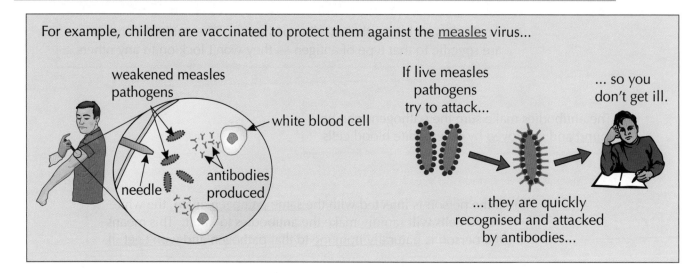

For example, children are vaccinated to protect them against the measles virus...

weakened measles pathogens

white blood cell

needle

antibodies produced

If live measles pathogens try to attack...

... they are quickly recognised and attacked by antibodies...

... so you don't get ill.

There are Pros and Cons of Vaccination

1. Pros

Vaccines have helped to control lots of communicable diseases that used to be common in the UK, e.g. polio.

1) A big outbreak of a disease is called an epidemic.
2) Epidemics can be prevented if lots of people are vaccinated.
3) That way, even the people who aren't vaccinated are unlikely to catch the disease because there are fewer people able to pass it on.

2. Cons

1) Vaccines don't always work — sometimes they don't give you immunity.
2) You can sometimes have a bad reaction to a vaccine (e.g. swelling or a fever).

Fighting Disease — Drugs

You've probably had to take some sort of <u>medicine</u> if you've been ill, e.g. cough remedies, painkillers.

Some Drugs **Get Rid of Symptoms** — Others **Cure** the Problem

1) Some drugs help to <u>get rid</u> of the <u>symptoms</u> of a disease, e.g. <u>painkillers reduce pain</u>.

2) But these drugs <u>don't kill</u> the pathogens that cause the disease.

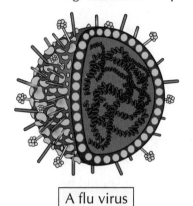

A flu virus

3) <u>Antibiotics</u> (e.g. penicillin) <u>kill bacteria</u>.

4) <u>Different antibiotics</u> kill <u>different types</u> of bacteria, so it's important to be treated with the <u>right one</u>.

5) The use of antibiotics has <u>greatly reduced</u> the number of deaths from communicable diseases caused by bacteria.

6) Antibiotics <u>don't destroy viruses</u> (e.g. <u>flu</u> viruses).

7) Viruses reproduce <u>using your own body cells</u>. This makes it very <u>difficult</u> to develop <u>drugs</u> that <u>destroy the virus</u> without <u>killing the body's cells</u>.

Bacteria Can Become **Resistant** to **Antibiotics**

1) Bacteria can <u>mutate</u> (change).

2) Some of these mutations cause the bacteria to become <u>resistant</u> to (not be killed by) an <u>antibiotic</u>.

3) <u>Resistant strains</u> (<u>types</u>) of bacteria, e.g. <u>MRSA</u>, have increased as a result of <u>natural selection</u> (see page 132).

Many **Drugs** First Came From **Plants**

1) <u>Plants</u> produce <u>chemicals</u> to <u>defend</u> themselves against <u>pests</u> and <u>pathogens</u>.

2) Some of these chemicals can be used as <u>drugs</u> to <u>treat</u> human diseases or <u>relieve symptoms</u>.

3) A lot of our <u>medicines</u> were found by studying plants used in <u>old-fashioned cures</u>. For example:

> 1) <u>Aspirin</u> is used as a <u>painkiller</u>. It was made from a chemical found in <u>willow</u>.
> 2) <u>Digitalis</u> is used to treat <u>heart conditions</u>. It was made from a chemical found in <u>foxgloves</u>.

4) Some drugs have come from <u>microorganisms</u>. For example:

> 1) Alexander Fleming found that a type of <u>mould</u> (called *Penicillium*) makes a <u>substance</u> that <u>kills bacteria</u>.
> 2) This substance is called <u>penicillin</u>.
> 3) Penicillin is used as an <u>antibiotic</u>.

5) These days, <u>new drugs</u> are <u>made</u> by the <u>pharmaceutical industry</u> (companies that make and sell drugs).

6) The drugs are made by <u>chemists</u> in <u>labs</u>.

7) The process of making the drugs still might start with a chemical <u>taken</u> from a <u>plant</u>.

Developing Drugs

New drugs are always being developed. But before they can be given to people like you and me, they have to go through a lot of tests. This is what usually happens...

There Are **Different Stages** in the **Development** of **New Drugs**

1) Once a possible drug has been discovered, it needs to be developed.
2) This involves preclinical and clinical testing.

Preclinical Testing

1) Drugs are first tested on human cells and tissues in the lab.
2) Next the drug is tested on live animals. This is to find out:

- Its efficacy (whether the drug works and has the effect you're looking for).
- Its toxicity (how harmful it is and whether it has any side effects).
- Its dosage (the concentration of the drug that works best and how often it should be taken).

Clinical Testing

If the drug passes the tests on animals then it's tested on human volunteers in a clinical trial.

1) First, the drug is tested on healthy volunteers. This is to make sure it doesn't have any harmful side effects when the body is working normally.
2) At the start of the trial, a very low dose of the drug is given. This dose is increased little by little.
3) If these results are good, the drugs can be tested on patients (people with the illness).
4) The optimum dose is found — this is the dose of drug that is the most effective and has few side effects.
5) To test how well the drug works, patients are put into two groups...

Group 1 is given the new drug.

Group 2 is given a placebo (a substance that's like the drug being tested but doesn't do anything).

6) The doctor compares the two groups of patients to see if the drug makes a real difference.
7) Clinical trials are blind — the patient doesn't know whether they're getting the drug or the placebo.
8) In fact, they're often double-blind — neither the patient nor the doctor knows who's taken the drug and who's taken the placebo until all the results have been gathered.
9) The results of these tests aren't published until they've been through peer review. This helps to prevent false claims.

Peer review is when other scientists check the work — see page 2.

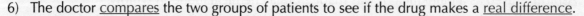

The placebo effect doesn't work with revision...

... you can't just expect to get a good mark and then magically get it. I know, I know, there's a lot of information to take in on this page, but just read it through slowly. There's nothing too tricky here — it's just a case of going over it again and again until you've got it all firmly lodged in your memory.

Warm-Up & Exam Questions

It's easy to think you've learnt everything in the section until you try the Warm-Up Questions.
Don't panic if there's a bit you've forgotten, just go back over that bit until it's firmly fixed in your brain.

Exam Questions

1 Many of the drugs used today first came from plants or microorganisms.

1.1 Draw **one** line from each drug to where it was originally extracted from.

Aspirin		Mould
Digitalis		Willow
Penicillin		Foxgloves

[2 marks]

1.2 State what aspirin is used for.

[1 mark]

1.3 State what penicillin is used for.

[1 mark]

2 The human immune system fights pathogens using a number of different methods.
One process for destroying pathogens is shown in **Figure 1**.

Figure 1

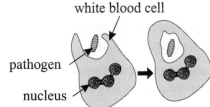

white blood cell

pathogen

nucleus

2.1 Name the process shown in **Figure 1**.

[1 mark]

2.2 Antibodies play a role in the immune response. Complete the sentences about antibodies.

Antibodies are produced by ....

They attach to specific antigens on the surface of the ....

[2 marks]

Exam Questions

3 A scientist is carrying out a clinical trial. **Grade 3-4**

3.1 What is a drug tested on in a clinical trial? Tick **one** box.

☐ human cells

☐ human volunteers

☐ live animals

☐ human tissue

[1 mark]

3.2 The clinical trial is double-blind. What is meant by 'double-blind'? Tick **one** box.

☐ The patient does not know whether they are receiving the drug or placebo, but the doctor does.

☐ All the patients are given a placebo first, followed by the drug.

☐ Neither the patient or the doctor know who is receiving the drug and who is receiving the placebo.

☐ All the patients are given the drug first, followed by a placebo.

[1 mark]

4 There are many different lines of defence in the human body that help to prevent pathogens from entering the blood. **Grade 4-5**

4.1 What is the role of the hairs and mucus in the nose?

[1 mark]

4.2 How do the cilia in the trachea and bronchi help to defend the body?

[1 mark]

4.3 What does the stomach produce to kill pathogens?

[1 mark]

5 Rubella is a communicable viral disease. **Grade 4-5**

The rubella virus is spread in droplets through the air when an infected person coughs, sneezes or talks.

The virus causes symptoms including fever and painful joints. The spread of the disease can be reduced by vaccination.

5.1* Explain how being vaccinated against rubella can prevent a person from catching the disease. In your answer, suggest why vaccinating a large number of people reduces the risk of someone who hasn't been vaccinated from catching rubella.

[6 marks]

5.2 Suggest **one** reason why some individuals may choose not to receive a vaccination against a disease.

[1 mark]

Photosynthesis

First, the photosynthesis equation. Then onto how plants use glucose...

Photosynthesis Produces Glucose Using Light

1) Photosynthesis uses energy to change carbon dioxide and water into glucose and oxygen.
2) It takes place in chloroplasts in plant cells.
3) Chloroplasts contain chlorophyll that absorbs light.
4) Energy is transferred to the chloroplasts from the environment by light.
5) Photosynthesis is an endothermic reaction.
   This means that energy is transferred from the environment during the reaction.
6) You need to learn the word equation for photosynthesis:

$$\text{carbon dioxide + water} \xrightarrow{\text{light}} \text{glucose + oxygen}$$

7) You also need to know the chemical symbols for the substances involved in photosynthesis:

carbon dioxide: CO_2 water: H_2O glucose: $C_6H_{12}O_6$ oxygen: O_2

Plants Use Glucose in Five Main Ways...

1) For respiration — This transfers energy from glucose (see p.93). This allows the plants to change the rest of the glucose into other useful substances.

2) For making cell walls — Glucose is changed into cellulose for making strong plant cell walls (see p.18).

3) For making amino acids — Glucose is combined with nitrate ions to make amino acids. Nitrate ions are absorbed from the soil. Amino acids are used to make proteins.

4) Stored as oils or fats — Glucose is turned into lipids (fats and oils) for storing in seeds.

5) Stored as starch — Glucose is turned into starch and stored in roots, stems and leaves.
   - Plants can use this starch when photosynthesis isn't happening.
   - Starch is insoluble (it can't be dissolved).
   - Being insoluble makes starch much better for storing than glucose. This is because a cell with lots of glucose in would draw in loads of water and swell up.

The Rate of Photosynthesis

The <u>rate</u> of photosynthesis can be <u>affected</u> by <u>a few</u> different things. These are called <u>limiting factors</u>...

Light, Temperature and CO$_2$ Affect the Rate of Photosynthesis

1) The <u>rate of photosynthesis</u> is affected by intensity of <u>light</u> (how bright the light is), concentration of <u>CO$_2$</u> and <u>temperature</u>.

2) Any of these things can become the <u>limiting factor</u> of photosynthesis.

3) A limiting factor is something that stops photosynthesis from happening any <u>faster</u>.

4) <u>Chlorophyll</u> can also be a <u>limiting factor</u> of photosynthesis.
   - The <u>amount of chlorophyll</u> in a plant can be affected by <u>disease</u>.
   - It can also be affected by <u>changes in the environment</u>, such as <u>a lack of nutrients</u>.
   - These factors can cause <u>chloroplasts</u> to become <u>damaged</u> or to <u>not</u> make <u>enough chlorophyll</u>.
   - This means they <u>can't absorb</u> as much <u>light</u>. The rate of photosynthesis is <u>reduced</u>.

Three Important Graphs for Rate of Photosynthesis

1. Not Enough Light Slows Down the Rate of Photosynthesis

1) At first, the <u>more light</u> there is, the <u>faster</u> photosynthesis happens.

2) This means the <u>rate of photosynthesis</u> depends on the <u>amount of light</u>. <u>Light</u> is the <u>limiting factor</u>.

3) After a certain point the graph <u>flattens out</u>. Here photosynthesis <u>won't go any faster</u> — even if you increase the light intensity.

4) This is because light is <u>no longer</u> the limiting factor. Now it's either the <u>temperature</u> or the amount of <u>carbon dioxide</u> that's the <u>limiting factor</u>.

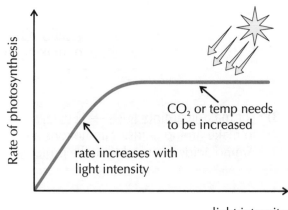

CO$_2$ or temp needs to be increased

rate increases with light intensity

light intensity

The amount of light is called light intensity.

'Photo' means light and 'synthesis' means putting together...

...so photosynthesis means 'putting together using light'. And the thing being put together is <u>glucose</u>. Well, I guess that's one way of remembering it... (Maybe just <u>learn</u> the <u>word equation</u> instead.)

The Rate of Photosynthesis

2. Too Little **Carbon Dioxide** Also Slows it Down

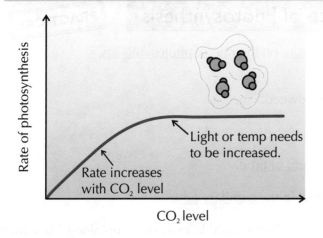

Light or temp needs to be increased.

Rate increases with CO_2 level

CO_2 level

1) The <u>more carbon dioxide</u> (CO_2) there is, the <u>faster</u> photosynthesis happens.

2) This means the amount of <u>CO_2</u> is the <u>limiting factor</u>.

3) After a certain point, photosynthesis <u>won't go any faster</u> because CO_2 is <u>no longer</u> the limiting factor.

4) If there's plenty of <u>light</u> and <u>carbon dioxide</u> then it must be the <u>temperature</u> that's the <u>limiting factor</u>.

3. The **Temperature** has to be Just Right

1) Usually, if the temperature is the <u>limiting factor</u> it's because it's <u>too low</u>.

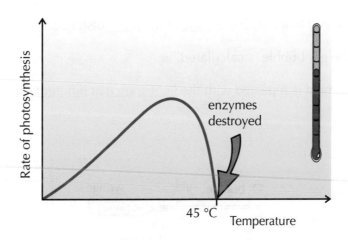

enzymes destroyed

45 °C   Temperature

2) This is because the <u>enzymes</u> (see page 42) needed for photosynthesis work more <u>slowly</u> at low temperatures.

3) But if the plant gets <u>too hot</u>, photosynthesis <u>won't happen at all</u>.

4) This is because the enzymes are <u>damaged</u> if the temperature's <u>too high</u> (over about 45 °C).

EXAM TIP

Make sure you know how to read from graphs

In the exam, you might have to describe what's going on in a graph of photosynthesis. <u>Don't panic</u> — just pay attention to the <u>axes</u>, to see what the graph is showing.

Measuring the Rate of Photosynthesis

It's practical time again. This one lets you see how changing <u>light intensity</u> affects the <u>rate of photosynthesis</u>.

Oxygen Production Shows the Rate of Photosynthesis

<u>Pondweed</u> can be used to measure the effect of <u>light intensity</u> on the <u>rate of photosynthesis</u>.
Here's how the experiment works:

1) A <u>ruler</u> is used to measure a <u>set distance</u> from the pondweed.

2) A <u>light</u> is placed at that distance.

3) The pondweed is left to photosynthesise for a <u>set amount of time</u>.

4) As it photosynthesises, the oxygen released will collect in the <u>capillary tube</u>.

5) At the end of the experiment, the <u>syringe</u> is used to draw the gas bubble in the tube up alongside a ruler.

6) The <u>length</u> of the <u>gas bubble</u> is <u>measured</u>.

7) The <u>length</u> of the gas bubble tells you <u>how much</u> oxygen has been produced during that amount of time. This means that the <u>longer</u> the gas bubble, the <u>faster</u> the rate of photosynthesis.

8) For this experiment, any <u>variables</u> that could affect the results should be <u>controlled</u>. E.g. the <u>temperature</u> and the <u>time</u> the pondweed is left to photosynthesise.

9) The experiment is <u>repeated</u> twice with the <u>lamp</u> at the <u>same</u> distance.

10) The <u>mean</u> length of the gas bubble is calculated.

11) Then the whole experiment is repeated with the <u>light source</u> at <u>different distances</u> from the pondweed.

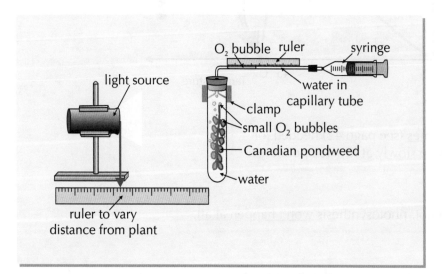

You can compare the results at different light intensities by giving the rate as the length of the bubble per unit time, e.g. cm/min.

Practicals — fun to carry out, not so fun to answer questions on

A good way to revise practicals is to scribble down as much as you can remember.
List what <u>equipment</u> is required and write out the <u>method</u> step-by-step.
You could even sketch a quick diagram of the <u>apparatus</u> all set up and practise labelling it.

Warm-Up & Exam Questions

Time for a break in the topic and some questions. Do them now, whilst all that learning is fresh in your mind. Using that knowledge will help you to remember it all, and that's what this game is all about.

Warm-Up Questions

1) What substance do chloroplasts contain that absorbs light?
2) Where does the energy for photosynthesis come from?
3) True or false? Photosynthesis is an exothermic reaction.
4) True or false? Glucose is used for respiration.

Exam Questions

1   Photosynthesis involves a number of substances.   (Grade 1-3)

1.1   Draw **one** line from each substance to its chemical symbol.

glucose		O_2
oxygen		H_2O
water		$C_6H_{12}O_6$

[2 marks]

1.2   Carbon dioxide is another substance involved in photosynthesis.
What is the chemical symbol for carbon dioxide?

[1 mark]

2   Photosynthesis produces glucose using light.   (Grade 3-4)

2.1   Complete the word equation for photosynthesis.

$$\text{carbon dioxide} + \text{.....................} \xrightarrow{\text{light}} \text{glucose} + \text{.....................}$$

[2 marks]

2.2   Plants use glucose to make a substance which strengthens their cell walls.
Which of the following substances strengthens cells walls? Tick **one** box.

☐ cellulose   ☐ oils   ☐ starch   ☐ fats

[1 mark]

2.3   Which of the following is another way that plants use glucose? Tick **one** box.

☐ making nitrates   ☐ storage as oils   ☐ making chlorophyll

[1 mark]

Exam Questions

3 Plants store glucose as starch. *(Grade 3-4)*

3.1 Which of the following is a characteristic of starch that makes it suitable for storage? Tick **one** box.

☐ it contains carbon ☐ it is soluble ☐ it is insoluble ☐ starch molecules are large

[1 mark]

3.2 Explain why plants use starch as a source of glucose when photosynthesis is **not** happening.

[1 mark]

4 A student investigated the effect of increasing carbon dioxide concentration on the rate of photosynthesis of a plant. The results are shown in **Figure 1**. *(Grade 4-5)*

Figure 1

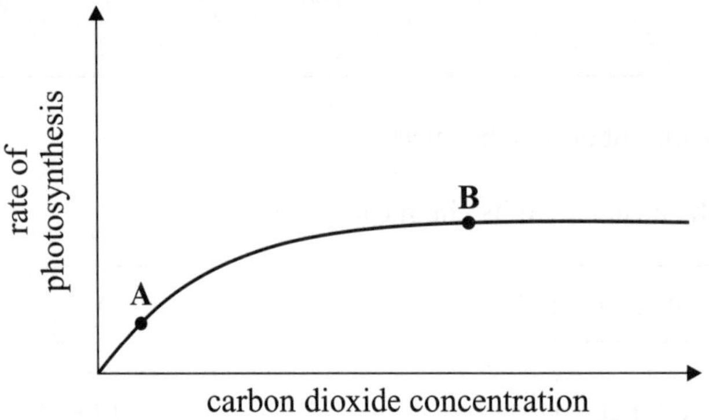

4.1 Describe the trend shown on the graph at point **A**.

[1 mark]

4.2 Give the limiting factor at point **A** on the curve.

[1 mark]

4.3 Explain why the curve is flattening out at point **B**.

[2 marks]

4.4 Explain why low temperatures limit the rate of photosynthesis.

[1 mark]

PRACTICAL

5 A student did an experiment to see how the rate of photosynthesis depends on light intensity. **Figure 2** shows some of her apparatus. *(Grade 4-5)*

5.1 How can the student measure the rate of photosynthesis?

[1 mark]

5.2 State the dependent variable in this experiment.

[1 mark]

5.3 State the independent variable in this experiment.

[1 mark]

5.4 State **one** factor that should be kept constant during this experiment.

[1 mark]

Figure 2

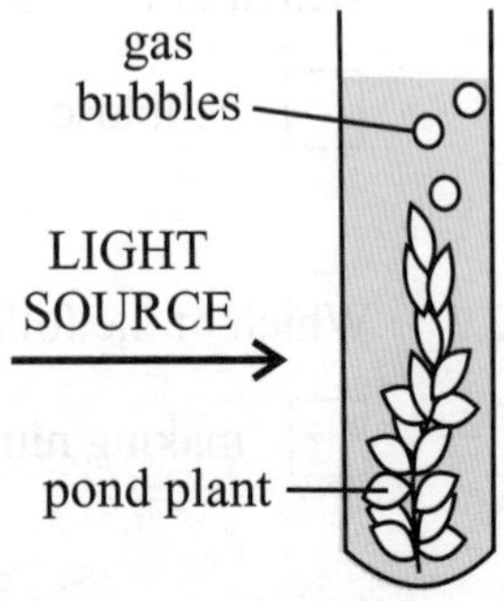

gas bubbles

LIGHT SOURCE

pond plant

Aerobic Respiration

You need <u>energy</u> to keep your body going. Energy comes from <u>food</u>, and it's <u>transferred</u> by <u>respiration</u>.

Respiration is NOT "Breathing In and Out"

1) <u>All living things respire</u>.
2) <u>Respiration</u> is the process of <u>transferring energy</u> from the <u>breakdown of glucose</u> (a sugar).
3) Respiration goes on in <u>every cell</u> in your body <u>all the time</u>.
4) The energy transferred from respiration is used for <u>all living processes</u> (everything a cell needs to do).

> <u>RESPIRATION</u> is the process of <u>TRANSFERRING ENERGY</u>
> <u>FROM GLUCOSE</u>, which goes on <u>IN EVERY CELL</u>.

5) Respiration is <u>exothermic</u>. This means it <u>transfers energy</u> to the <u>environment</u>.

Respiration Transfers Energy for All Kinds of Things

Here are <u>three examples</u> of how organisms <u>use</u> the <u>energy</u> transferred by respiration:

> 1) To build up <u>larger molecules</u> from <u>smaller</u> ones.
> 2) In animals, to <u>move</u> about.
> 3) In <u>mammals</u> and <u>birds</u>, to keep warm.

Aerobic Respiration Needs Plenty of Oxygen

1) <u>Aerobic respiration</u> is respiration using <u>oxygen</u>.
2) Aerobic respiration goes on <u>all the time</u> in <u>plants</u> and <u>animals</u>.
3) Most of the reactions in <u>aerobic respiration</u> happen inside <u>mitochondria</u> (see page 17).
4) You need to learn the overall <u>word equation</u> for respiration:

$$\text{glucose} + \text{oxygen} \longrightarrow \text{carbon dioxide} + \text{water}$$

5) You also need to know the <u>chemical symbols</u> for the substances involved:
glucose: $C_6H_{12}O_6$ oxygen: O_2 carbon dioxide: CO_2 water: H_2O

Anaerobic Respiration

Anaerobic respiration is just as important as aerobic respiration — especially when there's not enough oxygen...

Anaerobic Respiration is Used if There's Not Enough Oxygen

1) When you do hard exercise, your body sometimes can't supply enough oxygen to your muscles.
2) When this happens, they start doing anaerobic respiration as well as aerobic respiration.
3) Anaerobic respiration is the incomplete breakdown of glucose (the glucose isn't broken down properly).
4) Here's the word equation for anaerobic respiration in muscle cells:

$$glucose \longrightarrow lactic\ acid$$

5) Anaerobic respiration does not transfer anywhere near as much energy as aerobic respiration.
6) This is because the glucose has not combined with oxygen like it does in aerobic respiration.
7) The posh way of saying this is that the oxidation of glucose is not complete.

Anaerobic Respiration in Plants and Yeast is Slightly Different

1) Plants and yeast cells can respire without oxygen too.
2) Here is the word equation for anaerobic respiration in plants and yeast cells:

Yeast are single-celled organisms.

$$glucose \longrightarrow ethanol + carbon\ dioxide$$

3) Anaerobic respiration in yeast cells is called fermentation.
4) In the food and drinks industry, fermentation by yeast is of great value.
5) It's used to make bread. It's the carbon dioxide from fermentation that makes bread rise.
6) It's used to make alcoholic drinks (beer and wine). It's the fermentation process that produces alcohol.

Respiration releases energy from glucose

So... respiration is a pretty important thing — the energy transferred from glucose is used to make molecules that our cells need. When it comes to this topic, make sure you know the word equations from this page and the previous page and can compare the processes of aerobic and anaerobic respiration.

Exercise

When you exercise, your body responds in different ways to get enough energy to your cells.

When You **Exercise** You **Respire More**

1) Muscles need energy from respiration to contract (shorten).

2) When you exercise, some of your muscles contract more often.
This means you need more energy.

3) This energy comes from increased respiration.

4) The increase in respiration in your cells means you need to get more oxygen into them. To do this:

> 1) Your breathing rate (how fast you breathe) increases.
> 2) Your breath volume (how deep the breaths you take are) increases.
> 3) Your heart rate (how fast your heart beats) increases.

5) Increasing your breathing rate and breath volume gets oxygen into your blood quicker. Blood containing oxygen is called oxygenated blood.

6) Your heart rate increases to get this oxygenated blood around the body faster.

An unfit person's heart rate goes up a lot more during exercise than a fit person, and they take longer to recover.

Hard Exercise Can Lead to **Anaerobic Respiration**

1) When you do really hard exercise, your body can't supply oxygen to your muscles quickly enough.

2) This means your muscles start doing anaerobic respiration (see the previous page).

3) This is NOT the best way to transfer energy from glucose. This is because lactic acid builds up in the muscles, which gets painful.

4) Long periods of exercise also cause muscle fatigue. This is when the muscles get tired and stop contracting efficiently.

Anaerobic Respiration Leads to an **Oxygen Debt**

1) After anaerobic respiration stops, you'll have an "underline oxygen debt".

2) An oxygen debt is the amount of extra oxygen your body needs after exercise.

3) Your lungs, heart and blood couldn't keep up with the demand for oxygen earlier on.
So you have to "underline repay" the oxygen that you didn't get to your muscles in time.

4) This means you have to keep breathing hard for a while after you stop.

5) This gets more oxygen into your blood, which is transported to the muscle cells

Metabolism

Metabolism is going on <u>all of the time</u>. Right now. And now. Even now. Okay, you get the picture. Time to read all about it.

Metabolism is ALL the Chemical Reactions in an Organism

1) In a <u>cell</u> there are <u>lots</u> of <u>chemical reactions</u> happening <u>all the time</u>.

2) These reactions are controlled by <u>enzymes</u>.

There's more about enzymes on page 42

3) In some of these reactions, <u>larger molecules</u> are <u>made</u> from smaller ones. For example:

> 1) Lots of small <u>glucose</u> (sugar) molecules are <u>joined together</u> in reactions to form:
>   - <u>starch</u> (a storage molecule in plant cells),
>   - <u>glycogen</u> (a storage molecule in animal cells),
>   - <u>cellulose</u> (a component of plant cell walls).
>
> 2) <u>Lipid</u> molecules are each made from <u>one molecule</u> of <u>glycerol</u> and <u>three fatty acids</u>.
>
> 3) <u>Glucose</u> is combined with <u>nitrate ions</u> to make <u>amino acids</u>. These are then made into <u>proteins</u>.

4) In other reactions, larger molecules are <u>broken down</u> into smaller ones. For example:

> 1) <u>Glucose</u> is broken down in <u>respiration</u>.
>   - Respiration transfers energy to power <u>all</u> the reactions in the body that <u>make molecules</u>.
>
> 2) <u>Excess protein</u> is <u>broken down</u> in a <u>reaction</u> to produce <u>urea</u>. Urea is then <u>excreted</u> in <u>urine</u>.

Excreted is just a fancy word for 'released from the body'

5) The <u>sum</u> (total) of <u>all</u> of the <u>reactions</u> that happen in a <u>cell</u> or the <u>body</u> is called its <u>metabolism</u>.

It's still going on now

Remember, the energy for metabolism comes from <u>respiration</u>. This energy allows cells to make larger molecules from smaller ones, and to break larger molecules down into smaller ones. <u>Enzymes</u> are key to metabolism, so if you need a reminder about them, now is a good time to head back to page 42.

Warm-Up & Exam Questions

You know the drill by now — work your way through the Warm-Up questions, then the Exam Questions.

Warm-Up Questions

1) True or false? All living things respire.
2) What is anaerobic respiration in yeast cells called?
3) Give one way that the body gets more oxygen into cells during exercise.
4) What is excess protein broken down into?

Exam Questions

1 In the human body, respiration may be aerobic or anaerobic at different times. *Grade 3-4*

1.1 Which of the following is the word equation for anaerobic respiration in humans. Tick **one** box.

☐ glucose → lactic acid + carbon dioxide   ☐ glucose → lactic acid

☐ glucose → ethanol + carbon dioxide   ☐ glucose → ethanol

[1 mark]

1.2 The body uses anaerobic respiration during hard exercise.
Complete the sentences about anaerobic respiration during exercise.

Muscles start using anaerobic respiration when they don't get enough ....

This causes a build up of ....

After anaerobic respiration stops, the body is left with an oxygen ....

[3 marks]

2 Metabolism is a process in which larger molecules are made or broken down. *Grade 3-4*

Which of the following molecules is **not** formed by
joining lots of glucose molecules together? Tick **one** box.

☐ starch   ☐ glycogen   ☐ protein   ☐ cellulose

[1 mark]

3 Respiration is a process carried out by all living cells.
It can take place aerobically or anaerobically. *Grade 4-5*

3.1 Give **two** differences between aerobic and anaerobic respiration.

[2 marks]

3.2 Complete the word equation for aerobic respiration.

light

glucose + ... → carbon dioxide + ...

[2 marks]

Revision Summary for Topic 3 & Topic 4

Well, it's all over for <u>Topics 3 & 4</u> folks — I know you'll miss them, so here are some questions on them...
- Try these questions and <u>tick off each one</u> when you <u>get it right</u>.
- When you've done <u>all the questions</u> under a heading and are <u>completely happy</u> with it, tick it off.

Types of Disease (p.74-78) ☑

1) Give one way that pathogens can be spread. ☑
2) How can bacteria make us feel ill? ☑
3) True or false? *Salmonella* causes food poisoning. ☑
4) What type of disease is measles? ☑
5) Why does tobacco mosaic virus affect photosynthesis? ☑
6) What are the vectors for malaria? ☑

Fighting Disease (p.80-84) ☑

7) Give three ways that white blood cells can defend against pathogens. ☑
8) Why is it difficult to develop drugs that kill viruses? ☑
9) Give two things that drugs are tested on in preclinical testing. ☑

Photosynthesis (p.87-90) ☑

10) Where in a plant cell does photosynthesis take place? ☑
11) What is an endothermic reaction? ☑
12) Where are oils and fats stored in a plant? ☑
13) Why would a low concentration of chlorophyll limit photosynthesis? ☑
14) What is meant by a 'limiting factor' of photosynthesis? ☑
15) What effect would a low carbon dioxide concentration have on the rate of photosynthesis? ☑
16) Describe how you could measure the effect of light intensity on the rate of photosynthesis. ☑

Respiration and Metabolism (p.93-96) ☑

17) What is respiration? ☑
18) What is an exothermic reaction? ☑
19) Where do the reactions in aerobic respiration happen? ☑
20) What is the chemical symbol for water? ☑
21) What is the word equation for anaerobic respiration in yeast cells? ☑
22) Name two products of the food and drink industry that fermentation is needed for. ☑
23) What is meant by the term 'oxygen debt'? ☑

Homeostasis

Homeostasis — a word that strikes fear into the heart of many a GCSE student. But it's really not that bad at all. This page is a brief <u>introduction</u> to the topic, so you need to <u>nail all of this</u> before you can move on.

Homeostasis — Keeping **Conditions Inside Your Body Steady**

1) <u>Homeostasis</u> is the fancy word for keeping the <u>conditions</u> in your body and cells at the <u>right level</u>. This happens in response to <u>changes</u> inside and outside of the body.

2) This is really important because your <u>cells</u> need the <u>right conditions</u> to <u>work properly</u>.

3) This includes having the right conditions for <u>enzymes</u> to work (see p.42).

Your Body Uses **Control Systems** for **Homeostasis**

1) You have loads of <u>control systems</u> that keep the conditions in your body <u>steady</u>. For example, they keep your <u>body temperature</u>, <u>blood glucose level</u> and <u>water level</u> steady.

2) These control systems are <u>automatic</u> — you don't have to think about them.

3) They can control conditions in the body using the <u>nervous system</u> or <u>hormones</u>.

4) Control systems are made up of <u>three main parts</u>:

  - <u>receptors</u>,
  - <u>coordination centres</u> (including the brain, spinal cord and pancreas),
  - <u>effectors</u>.

5) When the level of something (e.g. blood glucose) gets <u>too high</u> or <u>too low</u>, its control system brings it back to <u>normal</u>.

  If the level is <u>too HIGH</u>, the control system <u>DECREASES</u> the level.
  If the level is <u>too LOW</u>, the control system <u>INCREASES</u> the level.

6) Here's how a control system works:

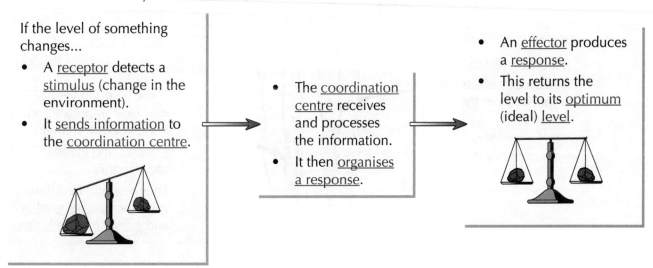

If the level of something changes...
- A <u>receptor</u> detects a <u>stimulus</u> (change in the environment).
- It <u>sends information</u> to the <u>coordination centre</u>.

- The <u>coordination centre</u> receives and processes the information.
- It then <u>organises a response</u>.

- An <u>effector</u> produces a <u>response</u>.
- This returns the level to its <u>optimum</u> (ideal) <u>level</u>.

Homeostasis is always happening without us thinking about it

Homeostasis is really important for keeping processes in your body working. It does this by keeping everything at the <u>right level</u>. Make sure you know what <u>receptors</u>, <u>coordination centres</u> and <u>effectors</u> do.

The Nervous System

Organisms need to <u>respond to stimuli</u> (changes in the environment). That's where the <u>nervous system</u> comes in — it picks up information from the environment and brings about a <u>response</u>.

The **Nervous System Detects** and **Reacts** to **Stimuli**

1) The <u>nervous system</u> means that humans can <u>react to their surroundings</u> and <u>coordinate their behaviour</u>.

2) The nervous system is made up of <u>different parts</u>:

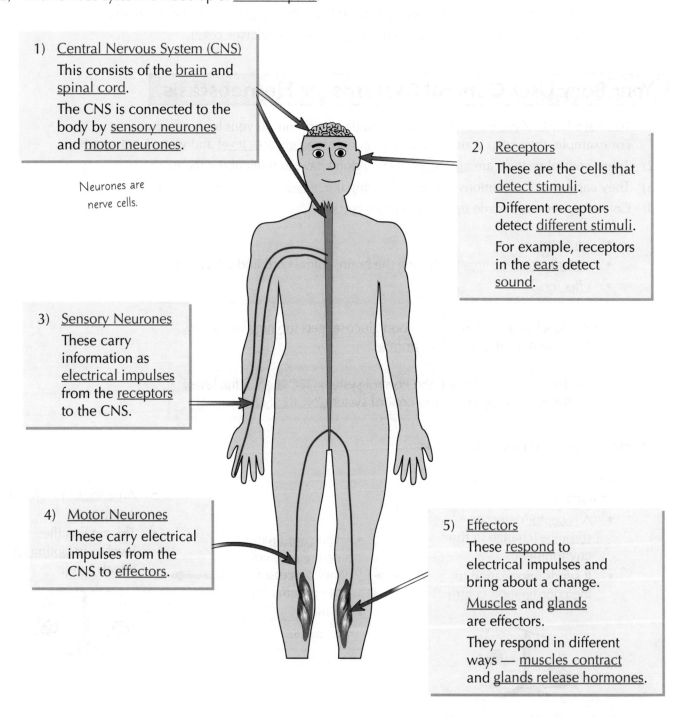

1) <u>Central Nervous System (CNS)</u>
This consists of the <u>brain</u> and <u>spinal cord</u>.
The CNS is connected to the body by <u>sensory neurones</u> and <u>motor neurones</u>.

Neurones are nerve cells.

2) <u>Receptors</u>
These are the cells that <u>detect stimuli</u>.
Different receptors detect <u>different stimuli</u>.
For example, receptors in the <u>ears</u> detect <u>sound</u>.

3) <u>Sensory Neurones</u>
These carry information as <u>electrical impulses</u> from the <u>receptors</u> to the CNS.

4) <u>Motor Neurones</u>
These carry electrical impulses from the CNS to <u>effectors</u>.

5) <u>Effectors</u>
These <u>respond</u> to electrical impulses and bring about a change.
<u>Muscles</u> and <u>glands</u> are effectors.
They respond in different ways — <u>muscles contract</u> and <u>glands release hormones</u>.

Learn the different parts of the nervous system

Don't be confused by the terms '<u>nervous system</u>' and '<u>central nervous system</u>'. The 'nervous system' includes <u>all</u> of the parts above, but the '<u>central</u> nervous system' means just the <u>brain</u> and <u>spinal cord</u>.

The Nervous System

Now for some detail about how the parts of the nervous system on the previous page work together.

The **Central Nervous System (CNS) Coordinates** the **Response**

1) The CNS is a coordination centre.
2) It receives information from the receptors and then coordinates a response (decides what to do about it).
3) The response is carried out by effectors.

For example, a small bird is eating some seed...

1) ...when it spots a cat coming towards it (this is the stimulus).
2) The receptors in the bird's eye are stimulated (activated).
3) Sensory neurones carry the information from the receptors to the CNS.
4) The CNS decides what to do about it.
5) The CNS sends information to the muscles in the bird's wings (the effectors) along motor neurones.
6) The muscles contract and the bird flies away to safety.

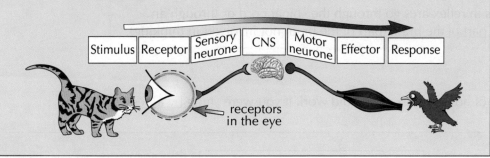

Stimulus | Receptor | Sensory neurone | CNS | Motor neurone | Effector | Response

receptors in the eye

Synapses Connect Neurones

1) A synapse is where two neurones join together.
2) The electrical impulse is passed from one neurone to the next by chemicals.
3) These chemicals move across the gap.
4) The chemicals set off a new electrical impulse in the next neurone.

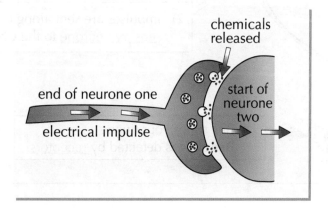

chemicals released

end of neurone one

electrical impulse

start of neurone two

Don't let the thought of exams play on your nerves...

Cover up the page and practise writing out the order of events from stimulus to response. Pay attention to names of the neurones — you don't want to be getting them mixed up in the exam.

The Nervous System

Neurones transmit information <u>very quickly</u> to and from the brain, and your brain <u>quickly decides</u> how to respond to a stimulus. But <u>reflexes</u> are even quicker...

Reflexes Help Prevent Injury

1) <u>Reflexes</u> are <u>automatic</u> responses — you don't have to <u>think</u> about them.

Reflexes are also called reflex reactions.

2) This makes them <u>really quick</u>.

3) They can help <u>stop you getting injured</u>.

4) The passage of information in a reflex (from receptor to effector) is called a <u>reflex arc</u>.

5) The neurones in reflex arcs go through the <u>spinal cord</u> or through an <u>unconscious part of the brain</u> (part of the brain not involved in thinking).

Here's an example of how a reflex arc would work if you were <u>stung by a bee</u>:

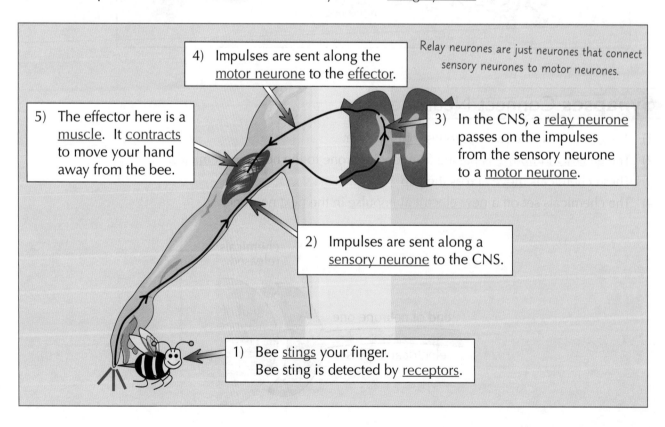

4) Impulses are sent along the <u>motor neurone</u> to the <u>effector</u>.

Relay neurones are just neurones that connect sensory neurones to motor neurones.

5) The effector here is a <u>muscle</u>. It <u>contracts</u> to move your hand away from the bee.

3) In the CNS, a <u>relay neurone</u> passes on the impulses from the sensory neurone to a <u>motor neurone</u>.

2) Impulses are sent along a <u>sensory neurone</u> to the CNS.

1) Bee <u>stings</u> your finger. Bee sting is detected by <u>receptors</u>.

Reflexes mean that you don't have to waste time deciding to respond

Reflexes don't involve your <u>conscious brain</u> at all when a <u>quick response</u> is <u>essential</u> — your body just gets on with things. If you had to stop and think first, you'd end up a lot more sore (or worse).

Investigating Reaction Time  PRACTICAL

Reaction time is the time it takes to <u>respond to a stimulus</u> — it's often <u>less</u> than a <u>second</u>. It can be <u>affected</u> by factors such as <u>age</u>, <u>gender</u> or <u>drugs</u>.

Reaction Time is How Quickly You Respond

1) Reaction time is the time it takes to <u>respond to a stimulus</u>.

2) It's often <u>less</u> than a <u>second</u>. This means it may be measured in <u>milliseconds</u> (ms).

3) It can be <u>affected</u> by factors such as <u>age</u>, <u>gender</u> or <u>drugs</u>.

You Can Measure Reaction Time

<u>Caffeine</u> is a <u>drug</u>. It can <u>speed up</u> a person's reaction time.
The <u>effect of caffeine</u> on reaction time can be <u>measured</u> like this...

1) The person being tested should sit with their arm resting on the edge of a table.

2) Hold a <u>ruler</u> upright between their thumb and forefinger. Make sure that the <u>zero end</u> of the ruler is <u>level</u> with their thumb and finger. <u>Don't</u> let them <u>grip</u> the ruler.

3) Then <u>let go</u> without giving any warning.

4) The person being tested should try to <u>catch the ruler</u> as quickly as they can.

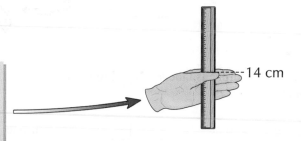

30 cm

0 cm

5) Reaction time is measured by the <u>number</u> on the ruler <u>where it's caught</u>.

14 cm

- The number should be read from the <u>top</u> of the person's <u>thumb</u>.
- The <u>higher the number</u>, the <u>slower</u> their reaction time.

6) <u>Repeat</u> the test several times then calculate the <u>mean distance</u> that the ruler fell.

7) Now give the person being tested a <u>caffeinated drink</u> (e.g. cola).

8) After 10 minutes, repeat steps 1 to 6.

9) You need to <u>control any variables</u> to make sure that this is a fair test. For example:

- Use the <u>same person</u> to catch the ruler each time.
- That person should always use the <u>same hand</u> to catch the ruler.
- The ruler should always be dropped from the <u>same height</u>.

As with any practical, you need to control the variables...

It's important that you measure a person's reaction time <u>before</u> they've had a caffeinated drink, as well as after — otherwise you won't be able to tell what effect the caffeine has had (if any).

Warm-Up & Exam Questions

Welcome to some questions. There are quite a few of them, but that's because they're pretty important...

Exam Questions

1   A man picked up a plate in the kitchen without realising it was hot, then immediately dropped it. **Figure 1** shows the reflex arc for this incident.

Figure 1

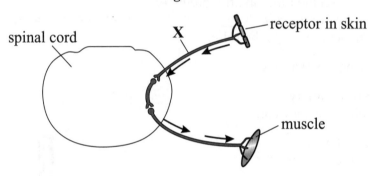

What type of neurone is labelled **X** in **Figure 1**?
Tick **one** box.

| ☐ motor neurone | ☐ sensory neurone | ☐ relay neurone |

[1 mark]

PRACTICAL

2   A student is taking part in an experiment to test reaction times. Every time a red triangle appears on the computer screen in front of her, she has to click the mouse.

2.1   Suggest what the stimulus is in this experiment.

[1 mark]

2.2   Suggest what the receptors are in this experiment.

[1 mark]

2.3   Suggest what the effectors are in this experiment.

[1 mark]

2.4   The student took the test three times. Her reaction time in test 1 was 328 ms.
Her reaction time in test 2 was 346 ms. Her mean reaction time was 343 ms.
Calculate her reaction time for test 3.

[2 marks]

The Endocrine System

The other way to send information around the body (apart from along nerves) is by using hormones.

Hormones Are Chemical Messengers Sent in the Blood

1) Hormones are chemicals released by glands. They're released directly into the blood.

2) These glands are called endocrine glands. They make up your endocrine system.

3) Hormones are carried in the blood to other parts of the body.

4) They only affect particular cells in particular organs (called target organs).

Hormones and Nerves Have Differences

Hormones and nerves do similar jobs — they both carry information and instructions around the body. But there are some important differences between them:

Nerves

1) Very FAST action.

2) Act for a very SHORT TIME.

3) Act on a very PRECISE AREA.

Hormones

1) SLOWER action.

2) Act for a LONG TIME.

3) Act in a more GENERAL way.

If you're not sure whether a response is nervous or hormonal, have a think about the speed of the reaction and how long it lasts.

Nerves, hormones — no wonder revision makes me tense...

Hormones control various organs and cells in the body, though they tend to control things that aren't immediately life-threatening (so things like sexual development, blood sugar level, water content, etc.).

The Endocrine System

Hormones are released by <u>endocrine glands</u>. There are a few examples you need to learn on this page.

Endocrine Glands Are Found in Different Places in The Body

PITUITARY GLAND

1) Sometimes called the '<u>master gland</u>'.

2) This is because it produces <u>many hormones</u> that regulate <u>body conditions</u>.

3) These hormones act on <u>other glands</u>. They make the glands <u>release hormones</u> that bring about <u>change</u>.

THYROID

1) Produces <u>thyroxine</u>.

2) This is involved in regulating things like the <u>rate of metabolism</u>, <u>heart rate</u> and <u>temperature</u>.

OVARIES (females only)

1) Produce <u>oestrogen</u>.

2) This is involved in the <u>menstrual cycle</u> (see page 110).

ADRENAL GLAND

1) Produces <u>adrenaline</u>.

2) This is used to prepare the body for a '<u>fight or flight</u>' response.

THE PANCREAS

1) Produces <u>insulin</u>.

2) This is used to regulate the <u>blood glucose level</u> (see next page).

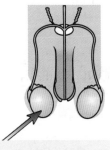

TESTES (males only)

1) Produce <u>testosterone</u>.

2) This controls <u>puberty</u> and <u>sperm production</u> in males (see page 110).

You need to know where these glands are in the body

Draw a rough outline of the human body and see if you can draw each of these endocrine glands onto it in the right place. Don't forget you need to remember both the testes and the ovaries.

Controlling Blood Glucose

You should remember from page 99 that homeostasis is all about keeping conditions inside the body stable. Blood glucose is controlled as part of homeostasis — insulin is an important hormone in this.

Insulin Reduces the Blood Glucose Level

1) Eating carbohydrates puts glucose (a type of sugar) into the blood.

2) Glucose is removed from the blood by cells (which use it for energy).

3) When you exercise, a lot more glucose is removed from the blood.

4) Changes in the blood glucose concentration are monitored and controlled by the pancreas.

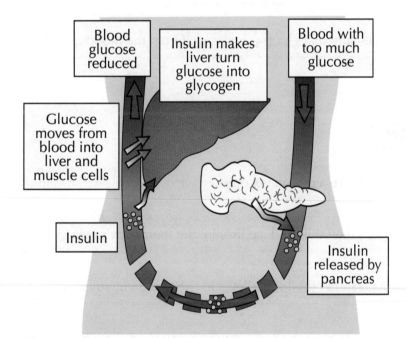

Blood glucose reduced

Insulin makes liver turn glucose into glycogen

Blood with too much glucose

Glucose moves from blood into liver and muscle cells

Insulin

Insulin released by pancreas

5) If blood glucose concentration gets too high, the pancreas releases the hormone insulin.

6) Insulin causes glucose to move into cells (so it removes glucose from the blood).

7) Glucose can be stored as glycogen.

8) Glucose is converted to glycogen in liver and muscle cells.

Glucose in the blood needs to be kept at a safe level

This stuff can seem a bit confusing at first, but if you learn that diagram, it should get a bit easier.

Controlling Blood Glucose

Sometimes, homeostasis goes wrong. Diabetes is an example of this.

With **Diabetes**, You **Can't Control** Your **Blood Sugar Level**

There are two types of diabetes:

Type 1 Diabetes

Large amounts of glucose in the blood can damage organs like the heart.

1) Type 1 diabetes is where the pancreas produces little or no insulin.

2) This means a person's blood glucose level can rise to a level that can kill them.

3) People with Type 1 diabetes need injections of insulin throughout the day.

4) This makes sure that glucose is removed from the blood quickly after the food is digested.

Type 2 Diabetes

1) Type 2 diabetes is where a person becomes resistant to their own insulin.

2) This means they still produce insulin, but their body's cells don't respond properly to it.

3) This can cause a person's blood sugar level to rise to a dangerous level.

4) Being obese (very overweight) can increase your chance of developing Type 2 diabetes.

5) Type 2 diabetes can be controlled by eating a carbohydrate-controlled diet.

6) This is a diet where the amount of carbohydrates eaten is carefully measured.

7) Type 2 diabetes can also be controlled by taking regular exercise.

Be prepared to interpret graphs in the exam

In the exam, you might be given a graph showing the effect of insulin on blood sugar level.
Don't panic — just study the graph carefully (including the axes labels) so you know exactly
what it's showing you. Then apply your blood sugar knowledge.

Warm-Up & Exam Questions

If these questions don't get your adrenaline pumping, I don't know what will. Better get started...

Warm-Up Questions

1) How do hormones travel to their target organs?
2) Which gland produces thyroxine?
3) True or false? Type 2 diabetes is where the pancreas produces little or no insulin.
4) Give one way that Type 2 diabetes can be controlled.

Exam Questions

1 Hormones are produced in endocrine glands.

Complete **Table 1** to show which endocrine glands the hormones are released from.

Table 1

Hormone	Gland the hormone is released from
Testosterone	
	Adrenal gland
Oestrogen	

[3 marks]

2 **Figure 1** shows how the body responds when the glucose concentration of the blood gets too high.

Figure 1

Step 1) Blood glucose level is too high.

Step 2) Insulin is released by the ....

Step 3) Insulin causes glucose to move from blood into cells.

Step 4) Liver and muscle cells convert glucose into ....

Complete **Step 2** and **Step 4** in **Figure 1**.

[2 marks]

Puberty and the Menstrual Cycle

The monthly <u>release of an egg</u> from a woman's ovaries is part of the <u>menstrual cycle</u>.

Hormones Cause Sexual Characteristics To Develop at Puberty

1) At <u>puberty</u>, your body starts releasing <u>sex hormones</u>.

2) These sex hormones trigger <u>secondary sexual characteristics</u>. For example, the development of <u>facial hair</u> in men and <u>breasts</u> in women.

3) Female sex hormones also cause <u>eggs</u> to <u>mature</u> (develop) in women.

4) In <u>men</u>, the main reproductive hormone is <u>testosterone</u>. It's produced by the <u>testes</u>. It stimulates <u>sperm production</u>.

5) In <u>women</u>, the main reproductive hormone is <u>oestrogen</u>. It's produced by the <u>ovaries</u>. Oestrogen is involved in the <u>menstrual cycle</u>.

The Menstrual Cycle Has Four Stages

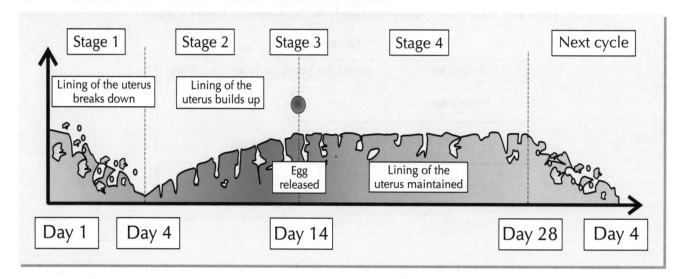

Stage 1

<u>Day 1 is when menstruation (bleeding) starts</u>. The uterus lining breaks down for about four days.

Stage 2

<u>The uterus lining builds up again</u> from day 4 to day 14. It builds into a thick spongy layer full of blood vessels. It's now ready to receive a fertilised egg.

Stage 3

<u>An egg develops and is released</u> from the ovary at day 14. This is called <u>ovulation</u>.

An egg is released once every 28 days.

Stage 4

<u>The wall is then maintained (kept the same)</u> for about 14 days until day 28. If no fertilised egg has landed on the uterus wall by day 28, the spongy lining starts to break down. The whole cycle starts again.

The Menstrual Cycle and Controlling Fertility

A set of hormones controls the menstrual cycle. Some of these hormones can be used to prevent pregnancy.

The Menstrual Cycle is Controlled by Four Hormones...

HORMONE	WHAT THE HORMONE DOES
FSH (Follicle-Stimulating Hormone)	Causes an egg to mature in one of the ovaries.
LH (Luteinising Hormone)	Causes the release of an egg (ovulation).
Oestrogen	These hormones are involved in the growth and maintenance of the uterus lining.
Progesterone	

Hormones Can Be Used to Reduce Fertility

1) Fertility is how easy it is for a woman to get pregnant.

2) Contraceptives are things that prevent pregnancy.

3) Hormones can be used in contraceptives — these are called hormonal contraceptives.

Oral Contraceptives Contain Hormones

1) Oral contraceptives are taken through the mouth as pills.

2) They stop the hormone FSH from being released.

3) This stops eggs maturing.

4) Oral contraceptives are over 99% effective at preventing pregnancy.

5) But they can have bad side effects.
For example, they can cause headaches and make you feel sick.

The hormones of the menstrual cycle can be controlled

Female or not, learn this stuff... till you know what hormone does what, and how oral contraceptives work.

Controlling Fertility

Oral contraceptives aren't the only way that hormones can be used to control fertility.

Some Hormonal Contraceptives Release Progesterone

1) Some hormonal contraceptives work by slowly releasing progesterone.

2) This stops eggs from maturing or being released from the ovaries.

3) Examples of contraceptives that work this way are:

Contraceptive patch

1) This is a small patch that is stuck to the skin.

2) It lasts one week.

The contraceptive patch releases oestrogen as well as progesterone.

Contraceptive implant

1) This is inserted under the skin of the arm.

2) An implant can last for three years.

Contraceptive injection

Each dose lasts two to three months.

Some Intrauterine Devices Contain Hormones

1) An intrauterine device (IUD) is a T-shaped device that's inserted into the uterus (womb).

2) It can stop fertilised eggs from implanting in the uterus wall.

3) Some types of IUD release a hormone.

Barriers Stop Egg and Sperm Meeting

1) Non-hormonal contraceptives (types that don't use hormones) stop the sperm from getting to the egg.

2) Barrier methods are one type of non-hormonal contraceptive. For example:

Condoms

1) Condoms are worn over the penis during sexual intercourse.

2) Female condoms are worn inside the vagina.

3) Condoms are the only form of contraception that will protect against sexually transmitted diseases.

There are many different types of contraceptives

There are a lot of options when it comes to contraception. There are even more on the next page...

More on Controlling Fertility

Using condoms isn't the only barrier method of contraception — diaphragms can also stop the sperm from reaching the egg.

Diaphragms

1) A diaphragm is a shallow plastic cup that fits over the entrance to the uterus.
2) It has to be used with spermicide (a chemical that disables or kills the sperm).
3) Spermicide can be used alone as a form of contraception. But when used alone, it is not as effective (it's only about 70-80% effective at preventing pregnancy).

There are **More Drastic** Ways to **Avoid Pregnancy**

Sterilisation

1) In females, sterilisation involves cutting or tying the fallopian tubes (tubes that connect the ovaries to the uterus).
2) In males, it involves cutting or tying the sperm ducts (tubes between the testes and the penis).
3) Sterilisation is permanent (lasts for life).

Natural Methods

1) Pregnancy may be avoided by not having sexual intercourse when a woman is at the stage of the menstrual cycle when she is most likely to get pregnant.
2) It's popular with people who think that hormonal and barrier methods are unnatural.
3) But it's not very effective.

Abstinence

1) The only way to be sure that sperm and egg don't meet is to not have intercourse.
2) This is called abstinence.

Some methods of contraception are more effective than others

You might be asked to evaluate the different hormonal and non-hormonal methods of contraception in your exam. If you do, make sure you weigh up and write about the pros AND the cons of each method.

Warm-Up & Exam Questions

Right then, another lot of pages down. Now there's just the small matter of answering some questions...

1) Name the hormone that stimulates sperm production in males.
2) Name the hormone that causes an egg to mature in the ovary.
3) What hormones does the contraceptive patch contain?
4) What is spermicide?
5) True or false? Only males can be sterilised to avoid pregnancy?

Exam Questions

1 During puberty, secondary sex characteristics develop. (Grade 1-3)

1.1 Give **one** example of a secondary sex characteristic.

[1 mark]

1.2 In females, ovulation begins to occur at puberty.
How often does ovulation usually occur?

[1 mark]

2 There are several methods that can be used to avoid pregnancy. (Grade 1-3)

Which of the following is a barrier method of contraception?
Tick **one** box.

☐ sterilisation

☐ diaphragm

☐ contraceptive implant

☐ contraceptive injection

[1 mark]

3 The menstrual cycle is controlled by several different hormones. (Grade 4-5)

3.1 What does the hormone oestrogen do?

[1 mark]

3.2 Which hormone causes the release of an egg?

[1 mark]

3.3 Hormones can also be used in contraception.
Explain how oral contraceptives prevent pregnancy.

[2 marks]

DNA

The first step in understanding <u>genetics</u> is getting to grips with <u>DNA</u>.

Chromosomes Are Really Long Molecules of DNA

1) <u>DNA</u> is the <u>chemical</u> that all of the <u>genetic material</u> in a cell is <u>made</u> up from.
2) It contains all the <u>instructions</u> to put an organism together and <u>make it work</u>.
3) A DNA molecule is made up of <u>two strands</u> of DNA coiled together. They make a <u>double helix</u> (a double-stranded spiral).
4) A DNA strand is a <u>polymer</u>. A polymer is something made up of <u>lots of smaller</u> pieces joined <u>together</u>.
5) DNA is found in the <u>nucleus</u> of animal and plant cells.
6) It's found in really long structures called <u>chromosomes</u>.

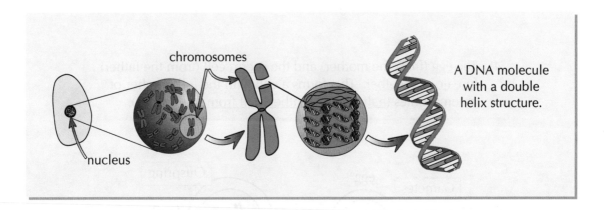

chromosomes

nucleus

A DNA molecule with a double helix structure.

A Gene Codes for a Specific Protein

1) A <u>gene</u> is a small <u>section</u> of DNA found on a <u>chromosome</u>.
2) Each gene <u>codes for</u> a <u>particular sequence</u> of <u>amino acids</u>.
3) These amino acids are joined together to make a <u>protein</u>.

Every Organism Has a Genome

1) <u>Genome</u> is just the fancy term for <u>all</u> of the <u>genetic material</u> in an organism.
2) Scientists have worked out the <u>whole human genome</u>.
3) <u>Understanding</u> the human genome is really important for <u>medicine</u>. This is because:

Inherited diseases are diseases caused by faulty genes and passed from a parent to their offspring.

1) Scientists can <u>find genes</u> in the genome that are <u>linked</u> to different types of <u>disease</u>.
2) If scientists know which genes are linked to <u>inherited diseases</u>, they can <u>understand</u> them better. This could help us to develop <u>treatments</u>.
3) Scientists can look at <u>tiny differences</u> in the genomes of different people. This can help them find out about the <u>migration</u> (movement) of certain populations of people around the world over history.

Sexual Reproduction

Reproduction is <u>very important</u> for all species — it's how they <u>pass</u> on their <u>genes</u> to the next generation.

Sexual Reproduction Produces Genetically Different Cells

1) <u>Sexual reproduction</u> is where genes from <u>two</u> organisms (a <u>father</u> and a <u>mother</u>) are mixed.

2) The mother and father produce <u>gametes</u> (sex cells). E.g. <u>egg</u> and <u>sperm</u> cells in animals.

3) The gametes are produced by <u>meiosis</u> (see 118). Each gamete contains <u>half</u> the number of <u>chromosomes</u> of a normal cell.

4) The <u>egg</u> (from the mother) and the <u>sperm</u> cell (from the father) <u>fuse</u> (join) <u>together</u>. This forms a cell with the <u>full</u> number of chromosomes (<u>half from the father</u>, <u>half from the mother</u>).

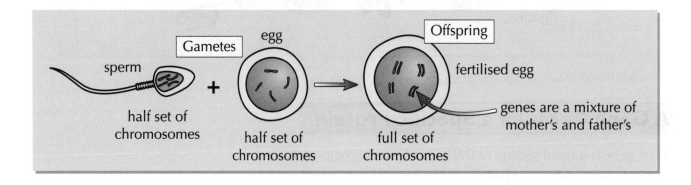

5) The offspring receives a <u>mixture</u> of genes, so <u>inherits features</u> from <u>both parents</u>.

6) This <u>mixture of genes</u> produces <u>variation</u> in the offspring.

7) <u>Flowering plants</u> can reproduce in this way <u>too</u>. Their gametes are <u>egg cells</u> and <u>pollen</u>.

Sexual reproduction mixes genes from two organisms...

When you're revising, make sure that you've got your head around sexual reproduction, <u>before</u> moving on to asexual reproduction — that way you don't confuse the two.

Asexual Reproduction

Some organisms use <u>asexual</u> reproduction to <u>pass</u> on their <u>genes</u>...

Asexual Reproduction Produces Genetically Identical Cells

1) <u>Asexual reproduction</u> happens by <u>mitosis</u>.

2) <u>One parent cell</u> makes a new cell by <u>dividing in two</u> (see page 28).

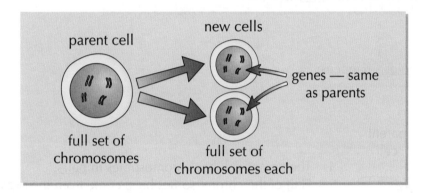

3) There's <u>no fusion of gametes</u>.

4) So there's <u>no mixing of genes</u>.

5) This means there's <u>no genetic variation</u> in the new cells.

6) Each <u>new cell</u> is <u>genetically identical</u> to the parent cell
— it has <u>exactly the same genes</u>. The new cell is a <u>clone</u>.

You might need to reproduce these facts in the exam...

The main messages about reproduction are that: 1) <u>sexual</u> reproduction needs <u>two</u> parents and forms cells that are <u>genetically different</u> to the parents, so there's lots of genetic variation. And 2) <u>asexual</u> reproduction needs just <u>one</u> parent to make <u>genetically identical</u> cells, so there's no genetic variation in the offspring.

Meiosis

Time now to learn about how <u>sperm</u> and <u>egg</u> cells are made...

Gametes Are **Produced** by **Meiosis**

1) Gametes only have <u>half the number</u> of chromosomes of normal cells.

2) To make gametes, cells divide by <u>meiosis</u>.

3) In humans, meiosis <u>only</u> happens in the <u>reproductive organs</u> (the <u>ovaries</u> in females and <u>testes</u> in males).

4) Here's how <u>meiosis</u> happens:

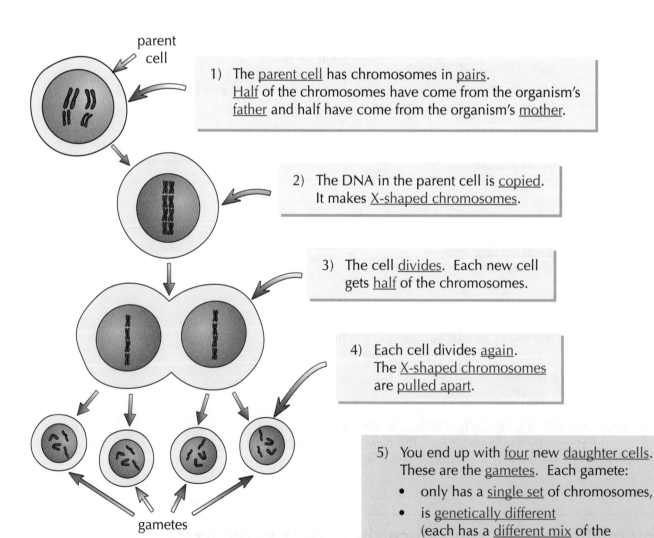

parent cell

1) The <u>parent cell</u> has chromosomes in <u>pairs</u>.
   <u>Half</u> of the chromosomes have come from the organism's <u>father</u> and half have come from the organism's <u>mother</u>.

2) The DNA in the parent cell is <u>copied</u>.
   It makes <u>X-shaped chromosomes</u>.

3) The cell <u>divides</u>. Each new cell gets <u>half</u> of the chromosomes.

4) Each cell divides <u>again</u>.
   The <u>X-shaped chromosomes</u> are <u>pulled apart</u>.

5) You end up with <u>four</u> new <u>daughter cells</u>.
   These are the <u>gametes</u>. Each gamete:
   • only has a <u>single set</u> of chromosomes,
   • is <u>genetically different</u>
     (each has a <u>different mix</u> of the <u>mother's</u> and <u>father's</u> chromosomes).

gametes

Fertilisation and Chromosomes

Now for a bit more about <u>gametes</u> and two <u>very</u> important little <u>chromosomes</u>...

Gametes Fuse to Make a New Cell

1) During fertilisation, two gametes <u>fuse together</u> (see p.116). This makes a <u>new cell</u>.

2) This new cell has the <u>normal number</u> of chromosomes.

3) The new cell <u>divides</u> by <u>mitosis</u> many times to produce <u>lots</u> of new cells. This forms an <u>embryo</u>.

4) As the embryo develops, these cells <u>differentiate</u> (see page 23). The cells become <u>different types</u> of <u>specialised cell</u> that make up a <u>whole organism</u>.

An embryo is an unborn baby at an early stage of growth.

Your Chromosomes Control Whether You're Male or Female

1) There are <u>23 pairs</u> of chromosomes in every human body cell.
2) <u>22</u> are <u>matched pairs</u> of chromosomes that just control your <u>characteristics</u>.
3) The <u>23rd pair</u> are labelled <u>XY</u> or <u>XX</u>.
4) They're the two chromosomes that <u>decide</u> your sex (whether you turn out <u>male</u> or <u>female</u>).

All <u>males</u> have an <u>X</u> and a <u>Y</u> chromosome: XY
The <u>Y chromosome</u> causes <u>male characteristics</u>.

All <u>females</u> have <u>two X chromosomes</u>: XX
The <u>XX combination</u> allows
<u>female characteristics</u> to develop.

5) Each sperm has <u>either</u> an X or a Y chromosome.
6) <u>All</u> egg cells have an X chromosome.

Now that I have your undivided attention...

Make sure you know what the X and Y chromosomes are before you head on to the next page...

Topic 6 — Inheritance, Variation and Evolution

X and Y Chromosomes

Genetic Diagrams Show the Possible Gamete Combinations

To find the <u>probability</u> (chance) of getting a boy or a girl, you can draw a <u>genetic diagram</u>. This type of genetic diagram is called a <u>Punnett square</u>.

1) Put the <u>possible gametes</u> (eggs or sperm) from <u>one</u> parent down the side. Put those from the <u>other</u> parent along the top.

2) Then in each middle square you <u>fill in</u> the letters from the top and side that line up with that square.

3) The <u>pairs of letters</u> in the middle show the possible combinations of the gametes.

4) There are <u>two XX results</u> and <u>two XY results</u>.

5) This means that there's the <u>same probability</u> of getting a boy or a girl — each one has a <u>1 in 2 chance</u> (which is the same as <u>50%</u>).

female gametes (eggs)

	X	X
X	XX	XX
Y	XY	XY

male gametes (sperm)

possible combinations of gametes...

...two males (XY) and two females (XX).

There's More Than One Type of Genetic Diagram

The <u>other type</u> of genetic diagram looks a bit more complicated, but it shows <u>exactly the same</u> thing.

1) At the top are the <u>parents</u>.

2) The middle circles show the <u>possible gametes</u> that are formed. One gamete from the female combines with one gamete from the male (during fertilisation).

3) The criss-cross lines show <u>all</u> the <u>possible</u> ways the X and Y chromosomes <u>could</u> combine.

4) The <u>possible offspring</u> you could get are shown in the bottom circles.

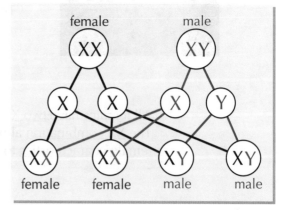

These diagrams aren't as scary as they look...

Most genetic diagrams you'll see sin exams concentrate on a <u>gene</u>, instead of a <u>chromosome</u>. But it's pretty much the same. Don't worry — there are loads of other examples on pages 123-124.

Warm-Up & Exam Questions

It's time to see how much you picked up about meiosis, reproduction and sex chromosomes...

Warm-Up Questions

1) True or false? There is variation in the offspring of sexual reproduction.
2) How many cell divisions take place in meiosis?
3) What combination of sex chromosomes do human females have?

Exam Questions

1   Sexual reproduction involves gametes fusing together to form offspring.
This is shown in **Figure 1**. The number of chromosomes in each cell is incomplete.

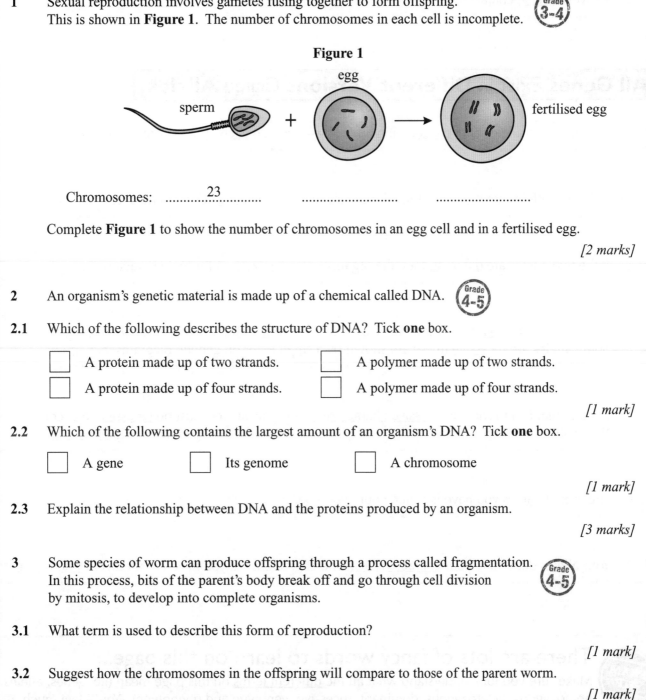

Figure 1

Chromosomes: 23 ....

Complete **Figure 1** to show the number of chromosomes in an egg cell and in a fertilised egg.

[2 marks]

2   An organism's genetic material is made up of a chemical called DNA.

2.1 Which of the following describes the structure of DNA? Tick **one** box.

☐ A protein made up of two strands.   ☐ A polymer made up of two strands.

☐ A protein made up of four strands.   ☐ A polymer made up of four strands.

[1 mark]

2.2 Which of the following contains the largest amount of an organism's DNA? Tick **one** box.

☐ A gene   ☐ Its genome   ☐ A chromosome

[1 mark]

2.3 Explain the relationship between DNA and the proteins produced by an organism.

[3 marks]

3   Some species of worm can produce offspring through a process called fragmentation.
In this process, bits of the parent's body break off and go through cell division
by mitosis, to develop into complete organisms.

3.1 What term is used to describe this form of reproduction?

[1 mark]

3.2 Suggest how the chromosomes in the offspring will compare to those of the parent worm.

[1 mark]

Genetic Diagrams

For those of you expecting to see a diagram or two on a page called 'Genetic Diagrams', prepare to be disappointed. You need to understand a bit more about what genetic diagrams show to start with...

Different Genes Control Different Characteristics

1) Some characteristics are controlled by a single gene. For example:

- mouse fur colour
- red-green colour blindness in humans.

2) However, most characteristics are controlled by several genes.

All Genes Exist in Different Versions Called Alleles

1) You have two alleles of every gene in your body — one on each chromosome in a pair.

2) If the two alleles are the same, then the organism is homozygous for that characteristic.

3) If the two alleles are different, then the organism is heterozygous for that characteristic.

4) Some alleles are dominant (these are shown with a capital letter on genetic diagrams, e.g. 'C').
   Some alleles are recessive (these are shown by a small letter on genetic diagrams, e.g. 'c').

5) For an organism to show a recessive characteristic, both its alleles must be recessive (e.g. cc).
   But to show a dominant characteristic, only one allele needs to be dominant (e.g. either CC or Cc).

6) The mix of alleles you have is called your genotype.

7) Your alleles determine your characteristics. The characteristics you have is called your phenotype.

There are lots of fancy words to learn on this page...

Make sure you fully understand what all the different terms on this page mean (i.e. genes, alleles, homozygous, heterozygous, dominant, recessive, genotype and phenotype). You'll feel much more comfortable going into the exam knowing that these words aren't going to trip you up.

Genetic Diagrams

This page is all about how <u>characteristics</u> are <u>inherited</u> — it involves drawing <u>genetic diagrams</u>.

Genetic Diagrams Can Show How Characteristics are Inherited

You can use <u>genetic diagrams</u> to show how <u>single genes</u> for characteristics are <u>inherited</u> (passed from parents to offspring). For example:

> 1) An allele that causes hamsters to have superpowers is <u>recessive</u> ("b").
> 2) <u>Normal</u> hamsters don't have superpowers due to a <u>dominant</u> allele ("B").
> 3) Two <u>homozygous</u> hamsters (<u>BB</u> and <u>bb</u>) are crossed (bred together). A genetic diagram shows what could happen:

A hamster with the genotype BB or Bb will be normal.
A hamster with the genotype bb will have superpowers.

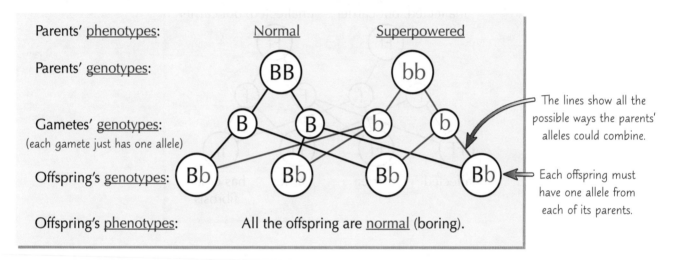

The lines show all the possible ways the parents' alleles could combine.

Each offspring must have one allele from each of its parents.

Punnett Squares are Another Type of Genetic Diagram

You can also show genetic crosses in a <u>Punnett square</u>.

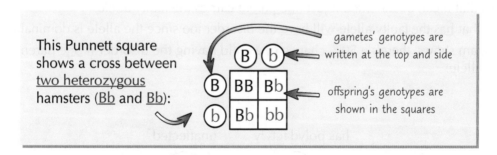

This Punnett square shows a cross between <u>two heterozygous</u> hamsters (<u>Bb</u> and <u>Bb</u>):

gametes' genotypes are written at the top and side

offspring's genotypes are shown in the squares

> 1) There's a <u>3 in 4</u> (75%) chance that offspring will be <u>normal</u>.
> 2) There's a <u>1 in 4</u> (25%) chance that offspring will have <u>superpowers</u>.
> 3) This gives a 3 normal : 1 superpowers <u>ratio</u> (<u>3:1</u>).

You can master genetic diagrams — you just need to practise them...

You should know how to <u>produce</u> and <u>understand</u> both of these types of genetic diagram before exam day.

Inherited Disorders

Inherited disorders are <u>health conditions</u>. They are caused by <u>inheriting</u> faulty <u>alleles</u>.

Cystic Fibrosis is Caused by a Recessive Allele

<u>Cystic fibrosis</u> is an <u>inherited disorder</u> of <u>cell membranes</u>.

1) The allele which causes cystic fibrosis is a <u>recessive allele</u>, 'f'.

2) Because it's recessive, people with only <u>one copy</u> of the allele <u>won't</u> have the disorder — they're known as <u>carriers</u>.

3) For a child to have the disorder, <u>both parents</u> must be either <u>carriers</u> or have the disorder <u>themselves</u>.

4) As the diagram shows, there's a <u>1 in 4 chance</u> of a child having the disorder if <u>both</u> parents are <u>carriers</u>.

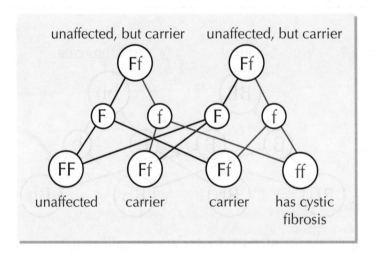

Polydactyly is Caused by a Dominant Allele

<u>Polydactyly</u> is an <u>inherited disorder</u> where a baby's born with <u>extra fingers or toes</u>.

1) The disorder is caused by a <u>dominant allele</u>, 'D'.

2) This means that it can be inherited if just <u>one parent</u> carries the faulty allele.

3) The <u>parent</u> that <u>has</u> the faulty allele <u>will have</u> the disorder too since the allele is dominant.

4) As the diagram shows, there's a <u>50% chance</u> of a child having the disorder if <u>one</u> parent has <u>one</u> D allele.

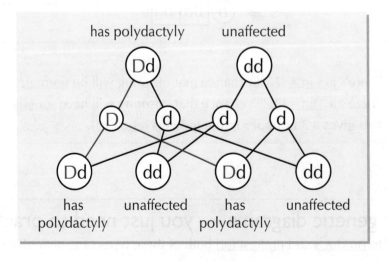

Family Trees

Just when you thought you'd finished with <u>genetic diagrams</u>, <u>family trees</u> show up...

Family Trees Show the Inheritance of Alleles

1) The diagram below is a <u>family tree</u> for <u>cystic fibrosis</u> (see previous page).

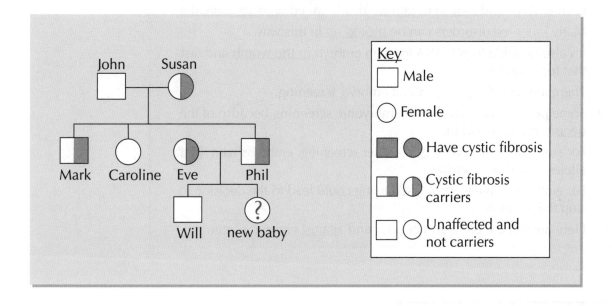

Key
- ☐ Male
- ○ Female
- ▨ ◖ Have cystic fibrosis
- ◧ ◐ Cystic fibrosis carriers
- ☐ ○ Unaffected and not carriers

2) From the family tree, you can tell that the allele for cystic fibrosis <u>isn't</u> dominant. This is because plenty of the family <u>carry</u> the allele but <u>don't</u> have the disorder.

3) There is a <u>25% chance</u> that the <u>new baby</u> will have the <u>disorder</u> and a <u>50% chance</u> that it will be a <u>carrier</u>. This is because both of the baby's parents are <u>carriers</u> (Eve and Phil are both Ff).

4) The case of the new baby is just the same as in the genetic diagram on page 124. The baby could be <u>unaffected</u> (FF), a <u>carrier</u> (Ff) or <u>have</u> cystic fibrosis (ff).

It's enough to make you go cross-eyed...

In the exam, you might get a family tree showing the inheritance of a <u>dominant</u> allele — in this case, there <u>won't be any carriers</u> shown. If you're struggling to work out a family tree in the exam, try writing the <u>genotype</u> of each person onto it — it might help you to understand it more easily.

Embryo Screening

Embryos can be screened for disorders, but not everyone agrees with it...

Embryos Can Be Screened for Inherited Disorders

1) During *in vitro* fertilisation (IVF), embryos are fertilised in a lab and then put in the mother's womb.
2) Before they are put into the mother, scientists can remove a cell from each embryo and look at its genes. This is called embryo screening.
3) Many inherited disorders can be picked up in this way.
4) It's also possible to get DNA from an embryo in the womb and test that for disorders.
5) There are lots of concerns about embryo screening.
6) Some people don't agree with embryonic screening because of the decisions it can lead to.
7) For embryos produced by IVF — after screening, embryos with 'bad' alleles would be destroyed.
8) For embryos in the womb — screening could lead to the decision to stop the pregnancy.
9) Here are some more arguments for and against embryo screening:

For Embryonic Screening

1) It will help to stop people suffering.
2) Treating disorders costs a lot of money.
3) There are laws to stop it going too far. At the moment parents cannot even select the sex of their baby (unless it's for health reasons).

Against Embryonic Screening

1) It suggests that people with genetic problems are not wanted. This could lead to them being treated unfairly.
2) There may come a point when people want to screen their embryos so they can pick the features they prefer. E.g. they want a certain eye colour or hair colour.
3) Screening is expensive.

Embryo screening — it's a tricky one...

It's great to think that we might be able to stop people from having inherited disorders that cause suffering, but there are many concerns to think about too. Try writing a balanced argument for and against embryo screening — it's good practice.

Warm-Up & Exam Questions

There's no better preparation for exam questions than doing... err... practice exam questions.
Hang on, what's this I see...

Warm-Up Questions

1) What is a different version of a gene called?
2) What does phenotype mean?
3) What is polydactyly?
4) Give one argument for embryo screening.

Exam Questions

1   Draw **one** line from each genetic term to its definition.

| heterozygous | | having two of the same allele |

| homozygous | | the mix of alleles in an organism |

| genotype | | having two different alleles |

[2 marks]

2   Cystic fibrosis is a genetic disorder caused by recessive alleles.

F = the normal allele   **f** = the faulty allele that causes cystic fibrosis

Figure 1 is an incomplete Punnett square showing the possible inheritance
of cystic fibrosis from one couple.

Figure 1

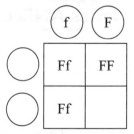

2.1   Complete the Punnett square to show the missing offspring's genotype
and the missing genotypes of the gametes.

[2 marks]

2.2   What proportion of the possible offspring are homozygous?

[1 mark]

2.3   State the phenotypes of the parents.

[2 marks]

Variation

You'll probably have noticed that not all people are identical. There are reasons for this.

Organisms of the **Same Species** Have **Differences**

1) Different species look... well... different — my dog definitely doesn't look like a daisy.
2) But even organisms of the same species will usually look at least slightly different.
3) These differences are called the variation within a species.
4) Variation can be huge within a population.

Variation Can be **Genetic**

Variation can be genetic — this means it's caused by differences in genes that are inherited.

Variation Can Also be **Environmental**

Variation can also be environmental — this means it's caused by the conditions in which an organism lives. For example:

1) A plant grown on a nice sunny windowsill could grow healthy and green.
2) The same plant grown in darkness would grow tall and spindly and its leaves would turn yellow.

Most Characteristics are Due to **Genes AND** the **Environment**

Most variation in phenotype is caused by a mixture of genes and the environment. For example:

1) The maximum height that an animal or plant could grow to is determined by its genes.
2) But whether it actually grows that tall depends on its environment (e.g. how much food it gets).

You can't blame all of your faults on your parents...

The genes that you inherit from your parents have a really important role in controlling what characteristics you have. However, the conditions in which you live usually affect your characteristics too.

Mutations

Sometimes the <u>sequence</u> of <u>DNA</u> can be changed. These changes are called <u>mutations</u>. Read on...

Mutations are Changes to the Genome

1) Sometimes, a gene can <u>mutate</u>.

2) A mutation is a <u>random change</u> in an organism's <u>DNA</u> that can be <u>inherited</u>.

3) Mutations occur <u>continuously</u>.

4) Mutations mean that the gene is <u>changed</u>.
   This produces a <u>genetic variant</u> (a different form of the gene).

5) Most <u>genetic variants</u> have <u>very little</u> or <u>no effect</u> on an organism's <u>phenotype</u> (its characteristics).

6) <u>Some</u> variants have a <u>small effect</u> on the organism's <u>phenotype</u>.
   They alter the individual's characteristics but only slightly. For example:

   - Some characteristics (e.g. eye colour) are controlled by <u>more than one gene</u>.
   - A mutation in <u>one</u> of the genes may <u>change</u> the <u>eye colour</u> a bit, but the difference might not be huge.

7) Very <u>rarely</u>, variants can have such a <u>big effect</u> that they lead to a <u>new phenotype</u>, e.g. cystic fibrosis.

8) A new phenotype may be <u>useful</u> if the <u>environment</u> that an organism lives in <u>changes</u>.

9) This is because sometimes a new phenotype makes an individual <u>more suited</u> to a new environment.

10) If this happens, the mutation can become common <u>throughout</u> the species <u>relatively quickly</u>. This happens by <u>natural selection</u> — see the next page.

Evolution

Evolution is very important. Without it we wouldn't have the great <u>variety of life</u> we have on Earth today.

> **THEORY OF EVOLUTION:** All of today's species have evolved from simple life forms that first started to develop over three billion years ago.

Only the **Fittest Survive**

1) <u>Charles Darwin</u> came up with a really important theory about <u>evolution</u> — it's called <u>evolution by natural selection</u>. It works like this:

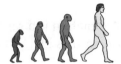

> 1) Organisms in a species show <u>wide variation</u> in their characteristics.

> 2) Organisms have to <u>compete</u> for <u>resources</u> in an ecosystem.

> 3) This means organisms with <u>characteristics</u> that make them better adapted to their <u>environment</u> will be better at <u>competing</u> with other organisms.

> 4) These organisms are <u>more likely to survive</u> and <u>reproduce</u>.

> 5) So the <u>genes</u> for the useful characteristics are more likely to be <u>passed on</u> to their <u>offspring</u>.

> 6) Over time, <u>useful characteristics</u> become <u>more common</u> in the population and the species <u>changes</u>. This is <u>evolution</u>.

2) Darwin's theory <u>wasn't perfect</u>. At the time he <u>couldn't</u> explain how <u>new</u> characteristics <u>appeared</u> or were <u>passed on</u>. Nowadays we have <u>evidence</u> to back up Darwin's theory, such as:

> 1) The <u>discovery of genetics</u> — it showed that characteristics are passed on in an organism's <u>genes</u>. It also showed that <u>genetic variants</u> (see page 129) produce the characteristics (<u>phenotypes</u>) that are better adapted to the environment.
> 2) <u>Fossils</u> — by looking at fossils of different ages (the <u>fossil record</u>), scientists could see how <u>changes</u> in organisms <u>developed slowly over time</u>.
> 3) <u>Antibiotic resistance</u> — how <u>bacteria</u> are able to evolve to become <u>resistant to antibiotics</u> also further supports <u>evolution</u> by <u>natural selection</u> (see page 132).

3) This means Darwin's theory of evolution by natural selection is now <u>widely accepted</u>.

Natural selection — the fittest pass on their genes...

Natural selection's all about the organisms with the <u>best characteristics</u> surviving to <u>pass on</u> their <u>genes</u> so that the whole species ends up adapted to its environment. It doesn't happen overnight though.

Evolution

Species need to <u>continue evolving</u> in order to <u>survive</u>. Sometimes this evolution creates a whole <u>new species</u>, but if a species can't evolve fast enough it might <u>die out</u> completely.

Evolution Can Lead to **New Species Developing**

1) Over a long period of time, the phenotype of organisms can <u>change</u> a lot because of <u>natural selection</u>.

2) Sometimes, the phenotype can change <u>so much</u> that a completely <u>new species</u> is formed.

3) New species develop when populations of the <u>same</u> species change so much that they <u>can't breed with each other</u> to produce <u>fertile offspring</u>.

Extinction is When **No Individuals** of a Species **Are Left**

Species become extinct for these reasons:

1) The <u>environment changes</u> too quickly (e.g. their habitat is destroyed).

2) A <u>new predator</u> kills them all (e.g. humans hunting them).

3) A <u>new disease</u> kills them all.

4) They can't <u>compete</u> with another (new) species for <u>food</u>.

5) A <u>catastrophic event</u> happens that kills them all (e.g. a volcanic eruption).

Evolution's happening all the time...

Many species evolve so <u>slowly</u> that there are <u>no big changes</u> in them within our lifetime. However, some species (e.g. bacteria) <u>reproduce really quickly</u>, so we're able to watch <u>evolution in action</u>.

Antibiotic-Resistant Bacteria

The discovery of <u>antibiotics</u> was a huge benefit to medicine — but they might not be a <u>permanent solution</u>.

Bacteria can Evolve and Become Antibiotic-Resistant

1) <u>Antibiotics</u> are drugs that <u>kill bacteria</u>.
2) Bacteria can become <u>resistant</u> to antibiotics by <u>natural selection</u>.
3) Here's what happens:

There's more about natural selection on page 130.

> 1) Bacteria can develop <u>random mutations</u> (changes) in their DNA.
> 2) These can lead to the bacteria being resistant to (<u>not killed by</u>) a particular <u>antibiotic</u>.
> 3) These <u>new strains</u> (types) of bacteria are called <u>antibiotic-resistant bacteria</u>.
> 4) The ability to <u>resist</u> antibiotics is a <u>big advantage</u> for the bacteria.
> 5) It means that the bacteria are able to <u>survive</u> in a host who's being <u>treated</u> to get rid of an infection.
> 6) So the antibiotic-resistant bacteria can <u>reproduce many more times</u>.
> 7) They <u>pass on</u> their gene for antibiotic resistance to their <u>offspring</u>.
> 8) The <u>gene</u> for antibiotic resistance becomes <u>more common</u> in the population over time — the bacteria have <u>evolved</u>.

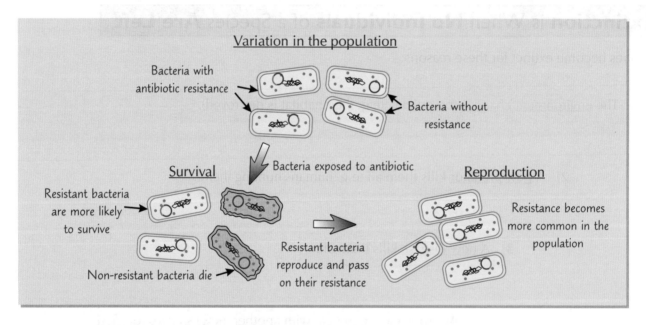

Variation in the population

Bacteria with antibiotic resistance

Bacteria without resistance

Survival — Bacteria exposed to antibiotic

Reproduction

Resistant bacteria are more likely to survive

Non-resistant bacteria die

Resistant bacteria reproduce and pass on their resistance

Resistance becomes more common in the population

4) Because bacteria are so <u>rapid</u> at <u>reproducing</u>, they can <u>evolve</u> quite <u>quickly</u>.
5) The antibiotic-resistant bacteria <u>keep reproducing</u>.
    This <u>increases</u> the <u>population size</u> of the antibiotic-resistant strain.

Antibiotic Resistant Bacteria Spread Easily

1) <u>Antibiotic-resistant bacteria</u> are a <u>problem</u> because:

> • There is <u>no effective treatment</u> for the infection.
> • People are <u>not immune</u> to the new strain.

2) This means that the antibiotic-resistant strain is able to <u>easily spread</u> between people.

More on Antibiotic-Resistant Bacteria

Antibiotic-resistance is getting <u>worse</u>. But there are ways to <u>fight it</u>...

Antibiotic Resistance is Becoming **More Common**

1) The problem of <u>antibiotic resistance</u> is getting <u>worse</u> because:

- Antibiotics are being <u>overused</u>.
- People <u>aren't</u> using antibiotics <u>correctly</u>.

2) '<u>Superbugs</u>' (bacteria that are resistant to most known antibiotics) are becoming more common.

> E.g. <u>MRSA</u> is a relatively common 'superbug' that's really hard to get rid of.

Antibiotics Need to Be **Used Sensibly**

There are a few things that can be done to <u>avoid</u> antibiotic-resistant bacteria forming:

1) Doctors should <u>only</u> prescribe antibiotics when they <u>really need</u> to.
- They <u>shouldn't be</u> prescribed for <u>non-serious conditions</u> or infections caused by <u>viruses</u>.

Antibiotics don't kill viruses.

2) You should take <u>all</u> the antibiotics a doctor prescribes for you.
- Taking the <u>full course</u> makes sure that <u>all</u> the bacteria are <u>destroyed</u>.
- This means that there are <u>none left</u> to <u>mutate</u> and develop into <u>antibiotic-resistant strains</u>.

3) The use of antibiotics by <u>farmers</u> should be <u>restricted</u> because:
- In farming, antibiotics can be given to animals to prevent them <u>becoming ill</u> and make them <u>grow faster</u>.
- This can lead to the development of <u>antibiotic-resistant strains</u> of bacteria in the animals.
- The antibiotic-resistant bacteria can then <u>spread to humans</u>.

We Can't Make **New** Antibiotics **Fast Enough**

1) Drug companies are working on developing <u>new antibiotics</u> that kill the resistant strains.
2) But there are problems:

- The rate of development is <u>slow</u>.
- The process is really <u>expensive</u>.

3) This means that we're unlikely to be able to <u>keep up</u> with the demand for <u>new drugs</u> to fight new antibiotic-resistant strains.

Warm-Up & Exam Questions

You need to test your knowledge with a few Warm-Up Questions, followed by some Exam Questions...

Warm-Up Questions

1) True or false? There is usually only a small amount of variation within a population.
2) True or false? Evolution never leads to new species developing.
3) What is meant by the term 'extinction'?
4) What is an antibiotic?

Exam Questions

1 **Figure 1** shows a type of stingray. The stingray's appearance looks like a flat rock. It spends most of its time on a rocky sea bed.

1.1 Use words from the box to complete the sentences about the evolution of the stingray's appearance.

Figure 1

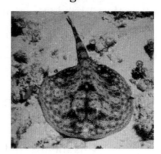

survive	generation	population
die	variation	similarity

The appearance of this stingray's ancestors showed ....

The ancestors that looked like flat rocks were hidden, so were more likely to ....

They were more likely to reproduce and pass their genes on to the next ....

[3 marks]

1.2 Suggest what caused some of the ancestors to look more like flat rocks than others.

[1 mark]

2 Helen and Stephanie are identical twins. This means they have identical DNA.

2.1 Helen weighs 7 kg more than Stephanie.
Explain whether this is due to genes, environmental factors or both.

[2 marks]

2.2 Stephanie has a birthmark on her shoulder. Helen doesn't.
Explain how this shows that birthmarks are **not** caused by genes.

[1 mark]

Selective Breeding

'Selective breeding' sounds like it could be a tricky topic, but it's actually quite simple.
You take the best plants or animals and breed them together to get the best possible offspring. That's it.

Selective Breeding is Very Simple

1) Selective breeding is when humans choose which plants or animals are going to breed.

2) Organisms are selectively bred to develop features that are useful or attractive. For example:

Selective breeding is also known as 'artificial selection'.

- Animals that produce more meat or milk.
- Crops with disease resistance (that are not killed by disease).
- Dogs with a good, gentle personality.
- Decorative plants with big or unusual flowers.

3) This is the basic process involved in selective breeding:

1) From your existing plants or animals select the ones which have the feature you're after.
2) Breed them with each other.
3) Select the best of the offspring, and breed them together.
4) Continue this process over several generations. Eventually, all offspring will have the feature you want.

4) Selective breeding is nothing new — people have been doing it for thousands of years.

5) This is how we ended up with edible crops from wild plants and domesticated animals like cows and dogs.

Selective breeding is just breeding the best to get the best...

Different breeds of dog came from selective breeding. For example, somebody thought 'I really like this small, yappy wolf — I'll breed it with this other one'. After thousands of generations, we got poodles.

Selective Breeding

Here's an **Example** of **Selective Breeding**:

A farmer might want his cattle to produce <u>more meat</u>.

1) <u>Genetic variation</u> means some cattle will have <u>better characteristics</u> for producing meat than others, e.g. a <u>larger size</u>.
2) The farmer could select the <u>largest</u> cows and bulls and <u>breed them</u> together.
3) He could then select the <u>largest offspring</u> and breed them together.
4) After <u>several generations</u>, he would get cows with a <u>very high meat yield</u>.

Selective Breeding Has **Disadvantages**

1) The main <u>problem</u> with selective breeding is that it <u>reduces</u> the number of <u>different alleles</u> in a population.

There's more on alleles on page 122.

2) This is because the "<u>best</u>" animals or plants are always used for breeding, and they are all <u>closely related</u> — this is known as <u>inbreeding</u>.

3) This means there's more chance of selectively bred organisms having <u>health problems</u> caused by their <u>genes</u>, e.g. they may inherit harmful <u>genetic defects</u>.

4) There can also be serious problems if a <u>new disease</u> appears.

5) This is because it's less likely that individuals in the population will have <u>alleles</u> that make them <u>resistant</u> to the disease.

6) So, if <u>one</u> individual is affected by the disease, <u>the rest</u> are <u>also</u> likely to be affected.

Selective breeding has its pros bred cons...

Selective breeding has already been producing good results for thousands of years, but it's still important that farmers and other people working in agriculture are aware of the disadvantages. They need to look at the evidence and weigh up the pros and cons before coming to a decision.

Genetic Engineering

As well as selective breeding, humans can also use <u>genetic engineering</u> to <u>control</u> an organism's <u>features</u>.

Genetic Engineering Involves Changing an Organism's DNA

1) <u>Genetic engineering</u> is used to give organisms <u>new</u> and <u>useful characteristics</u>.
2) It involves <u>cutting a gene</u> out of one organism and <u>putting it into</u> another organism's cells.
3) Organisms that have had a new gene <u>inserted</u> are called <u>genetically modified</u> (GM) organisms.

Genetic Engineering is Useful in Agriculture and Medicine

In Agriculture:

1) <u>Crops</u> can be genetically engineered — this makes <u>genetically modified (GM) crops</u>.
2) They may be genetically engineered to be <u>resistant to herbicides</u> (chemicals that kill plants). This means that farmers can <u>spray</u> their crops to <u>kill weeds</u>, <u>without</u> affecting the crop itself.
3) Crops can also be genetically engineered to be resistant to <u>insects</u> or <u>disease</u>. Or they can be made to grow <u>bigger and better fruit</u>.
4) These things can <u>increase crop yield</u> (the amount of food produced).

In Medicine:

1) <u>Bacteria</u> can be genetically engineered to produce <u>human insulin</u>. This can be used to treat <u>diabetes</u> (see p.108).
2) Treatments using genetic modification for <u>inherited diseases</u> are being researched.

But There are Some Concerns About Genetic Engineering

There are <u>concerns</u> about using genetic engineering in <u>animals</u>:

1) It can be hard to <u>predict</u> how changing an animal's DNA will affect the animal.
2) Many genetically modified embryos <u>don't survive</u>.
3) Some genetically modified <u>animals</u> also suffer from <u>health problems</u> later in life.

There are also <u>concerns</u> about growing <u>GM crops</u>:

1) Some people say that growing GM crops will affect the <u>number</u> of <u>wild flowers</u>. This could also affect the <u>population of insects</u>.
2) Some people are worried that we <u>might not understand</u> the effects of GM crops on <u>human health</u>.

Warm-Up & Exam Questions

By doing these Warm-Up and Exam Questions, you'll soon find out if you've got the basic facts straight.

Warm-Up Questions

1) True or false? Genetic engineering involves changing an organism's DNA.
2) What is the name given to crops that have been genetically engineered?
3) Name one useful product that humans have genetically modified bacteria to produce.

Exam Questions

1   A farmer wants to use selective breeding to improve disease resistance in his crops.

Use the words from the box to complete the sentences about the disadvantages of selective breeding.

| chromosomes | health problems | better characteristics |
| alleles | more resistant | less resistant |

In a population of selectively bred plants, there will be fewer different ....

This means if a new disease appears, the plants may be ....

Due to inbreeding, there's also more chance of selectively bred plants having ....

[3 marks]

2   Organisms can be genetically modified.
This means an organism's genes can be altered to alter its characteristics.

2.1   Plants can be genetically modified to become more resistant to disease.
Suggest **one** other useful way that plants can be genetically modified.

[1 mark]

2.2   Some people think that it is wrong to genetically modify crop plants.
Give **one** objection that a person might have.

[1 mark]

3   Cows can be selectively bred to produce offspring that produce a high milk yield.
Table 1 shows the average milk yield over three generations for a population of cows.

Table 1

Generation	Average milk yield per cow in litres per year
1	5000
2	5375
3	5750

3.1   Calculate the percentage change in average milk yield from generation **2** to generation **3**.

[2 marks]

3.2*   Describe the method the farmer used to selectively breed cows to produce a higher milk yield.

[4 marks]

Fossils

Fossils are great. If they're <u>well-preserved</u>, you can see what really old creatures <u>looked</u> like.

Fossils are the Remains of Plants and Animals

1) Fossils are the <u>remains</u> of organisms from <u>many thousands of years ago</u>. They're found in <u>rocks</u>.
2) They provide the <u>evidence</u> that organisms lived ages ago.
3) Fossils can tell us a lot about <u>how much</u> or <u>how little</u> organisms have <u>changed</u> (<u>evolved</u>) over time.
4) Fossils form in rocks in one of <u>three</u> ways:

1. From gradual replacement by minerals (Most fossils happen this way.)

1) Things like <u>teeth</u>, <u>shells</u> and <u>bones</u> don't easily decay.
2) This means they can last a <u>long time</u> when <u>buried</u>.
3) When they do decay, they get <u>replaced by minerals</u>.
4) The minerals form a <u>rock-like substance</u> shaped like the original hard part.

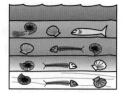

2. From casts and impressions

1) Fossils can be formed when an organism is <u>buried</u> in a <u>soft</u> material like <u>clay</u>.
    The clay <u>hardens</u> around it and the organism <u>decays</u>. The organism leaves a
    <u>cast</u> of itself. An animal's <u>burrow</u> or a plant's <u>roots</u> can also be preserved as casts.
2) Things like <u>footprints</u> are <u>pressed</u> into soft materials. This leaves an <u>impression</u> when they harden.

3. From preservation in places where no decay happens

1) <u>Decay microbes</u> only work if there's <u>oxygen</u>, <u>moisture</u>, <u>warmth</u> and the right <u>pH</u>.
2) In <u>some substances</u> these conditions <u>aren't</u> all <u>present</u>, so decay
    doesn't happen. For example, there's <u>no oxygen</u> or <u>moisture</u>
    in <u>amber</u> so decay organisms can't survive.

A preserved organism in amber.

But No One Knows How Life Began

1) Fossils show <u>how much</u> or <u>how little</u> different organisms have changed (<u>evolved</u>) as life has developed on Earth over millions of years.
2) There are lots of <u>hypotheses</u> (see p.2) suggesting how life first came into being. For example:

- Maybe the <u>first life forms</u> appeared in a <u>swamp</u> (or under the <u>sea</u>) here on <u>Earth</u>.
- Or maybe simple carbon molecules were brought here on <u>comets</u> and developed into simple life forms.

But no one really knows.

3) These hypotheses can't be supported or disproved because there's a <u>lack</u> of <u>valid</u> evidence.
4) There's a lack of evidence because many early organisms were <u>soft-bodied</u>.
    Soft tissue tends to decay away <u>completely</u>. So the fossil record is <u>incomplete</u> (unfinished).
5) Plus, fossils that did form millions of years ago may have been <u>destroyed</u> by <u>geological activity</u>.
    E.g. the movement of tectonic plates may have <u>crushed</u> fossils already formed in the rock.

Classification

People really seem to like <u>putting things</u> into <u>groups</u> — biologists certainly do anyway...

Classification is Organising **Living Organisms** into Groups

1) In the past, organisms were <u>classified</u> according to <u>characteristics</u> you can see (like number of legs). They were also classified by the <u>structures</u> that make them up (like mitochondria in cells).

2) The more similar two organisms <u>appeared</u>, the more <u>closely related</u> they were thought to be.

3) These characteristics were used to classify organisms in the <u>five kingdom classification system</u>.

4) In this system, living things are divided into <u>five groups</u> called <u>kingdoms</u>. These are:

- <u>Animals</u> — fish, mammals, reptiles, etc.
- <u>Plants</u> — grasses, trees, etc.
- <u>Fungi</u> — mushrooms and toadstools, yeasts, all that mouldy stuff on your loaf of bread.
- <u>Prokaryotes</u> — all <u>single-celled</u> organisms <u>without</u> a nucleus.
- <u>Protists</u> — <u>eukaryotic single-celled</u> organisms.

There's more on prokaryotes and eukaryotes on p.17.

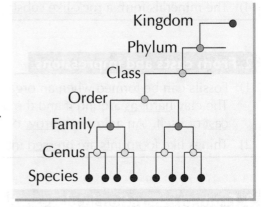

5) The <u>kingdoms</u> are then split into smaller and smaller groups.

6) These groups are <u>phylum</u>, <u>class</u>, <u>order</u>, <u>family</u>, <u>genus</u> and <u>species</u>.

7) The five kingdom classification system was made up by <u>Carl Linnaeus</u>.

Classification Systems **Change** Over Time

1) Over time, our knowledge of the <u>processes</u> taking place inside organisms has developed.

2) <u>Microscopes</u> have also <u>improved</u> over time. This has allowed us to find out more about the <u>internal structures</u> of organisms.

3) Using this new knowledge, scientists made <u>new</u> models of classification.

4) One of these new models was the <u>three-domain system</u>. It was made up by <u>Carl Woese</u>.

5) He used evidence from <u>analysing chemicals</u> to come up with the system.

6) It showed him that some species were <u>less closely related</u> than first thought.

7) Here's how the three-domain system works:

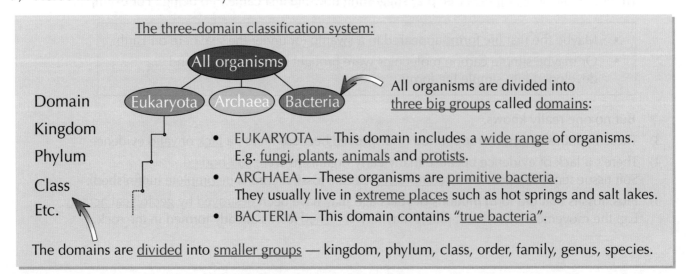

The three-domain classification system:

All organisms are divided into <u>three big groups</u> called <u>domains</u>:

- EUKARYOTA — This domain includes a <u>wide range</u> of organisms. E.g. <u>fungi</u>, <u>plants</u>, <u>animals</u> and <u>protists</u>.
- ARCHAEA — These organisms are <u>primitive bacteria</u>. They usually live in <u>extreme places</u> such as hot springs and salt lakes.
- BACTERIA — This domain contains "<u>true bacteria</u>".

The domains are <u>divided</u> into <u>smaller groups</u> — kingdom, phylum, class, order, family, genus, species.

Classification

A bit of a <u>Latin</u> lesson for you now. And a diagram of a <u>funny-looking tree</u>.

Organisms Are **Named** According to the **Binomial System**

1) In the binomial system, every organism is given its own <u>two-part</u> Latin name.
2) The <u>first</u> part refers to the <u>genus</u> that the organism belongs to.
   This gives you information on the organism's <u>ancestry</u> (the organisms it's related to).
3) The <u>second</u> part refers to the <u>species</u>.

E.g. humans are known as *Homo sapiens*.

'*Homo*' is the <u>genus</u>...   ...and '*sapiens*' is the <u>species</u>.

Evolutionary Trees Show **Relationships**

1) Evolutionary trees show how scientists think <u>different species</u> are <u>related</u>.
2) They show <u>common ancestors</u> and relationships between species.
3) The more <u>recent</u> the common ancestor, the more <u>closely related</u> the two species.
   Also, the <u>more characteristics</u> they are likely to <u>share</u>.
4) Scientists look at lots of different types of data to <u>work out</u> these relationships.
   For example:

   - For <u>living</u> organisms, they use <u>current classification data</u>.
   - For <u>extinct</u> species, they use information from the <u>fossil record</u> (see page 130).

   Extinct species are species that don't exist any more.

5) Here's an example of an evolutionary tree:

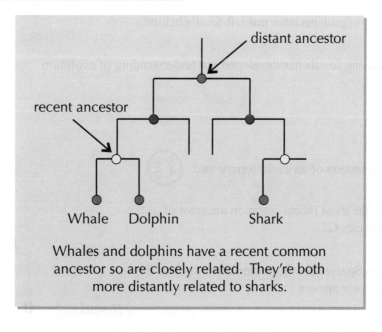

Whales and dolphins have a recent common ancestor so are closely related. They're both more distantly related to sharks.

Warm-Up & Exam Questions

The end of the topic is in sight now — just a few more questions to check you've been paying attention.

Warm-Up Questions

1) True or false? The fossil record is incomplete.
2) True or false? Carl Linnaeus classified organisms based on their characteristics.
3) In the binomial naming system, what does the first part of a name refer to?
4) In the binomial naming system, what does the second part of a name refer to?

Exam Questions

1 Scientists organise living organisms into groups. *(Grade 1-3)*

1.1 Which of the following is **not** a domain of the three-domain classification system? Tick **one** box.

☐ Plants ☐ Eukaryota ☐ Prokaryotes ☐ Archaea

[1 mark]

1.2 Which of the following scientists developed the three-domain classification system?
Tick **one** box.

☐ Charles Darwin ☐ Carl Linnaeus ☐ Carl Woese

[1 mark]

2 Fossils are the remains of plants and animals. *(Grade 4-5)*

2.1 Describe **one** way that fossils can be formed.

[1 mark]

2.2 Explain why many organisms have **not** left fossils behind.

[2 marks]

2.3 Explain how studying fossils has developed our understanding of evolution.

[1 mark]

3 **Figure 1** shows a section of an evolutionary tree. *(Grade 4-5)*

Figure 1

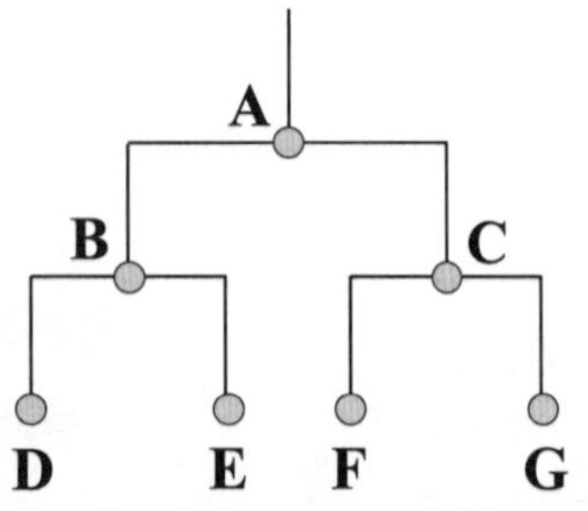

3.1 Which species is the most recent common ancestor of
Species **F** and Species **G**?

[1 mark]

3.2 Would you expect Species **D** to look similar to Species **E**?
Give a reason for your answer.

[1 mark]

Revision Summary for Topic 5 & Topic 6

So you've finished <u>Topics 5 and 6</u> — hoorah. Now here's a page full of questions to test your knowledge.
- Try these questions and <u>tick off each one</u> when you <u>get it right</u>.
- When you've done <u>all the questions</u> under a heading and are <u>completely happy</u> with it, tick it off.

Homeostasis and the Nervous System (p.99-103) ☑
1) What is homeostasis? ☑
2) What makes up the central nervous system? ☑
3) What is a synapse? ☑
4) What is the purpose of a reflex action? ☑
5) Name one factor that can affect reaction time. ☑

Hormones in Humans (p.105-113) ☑
6) Give two differences between nervous and hormonal responses. ☑
7) Name the hormone that reduces the blood glucose concentration. ☑
8) What does luteinising hormone (LH) do? ☑
9) What hormone does the contraceptive injection contain? ☑
10) Which of the following is a hormonal contraceptive — condom, implant or diaphragm? ☑

DNA, Genes, Reproduction, Meiosis and Sex Chromosomes (p.115-120) ☑
11) What do genes code for? ☑
12) What is the name for all of the genetic material in an organism? ☑
13) Name the male and female gametes of animals. ☑
14) State the type of cell division used to make gametes in humans. ☑
15) What is the probability that offspring will have the XX combination of sex chromosomes? ☑

Genetic Diagrams and Inherited Disorders (p.122-126) ☑
16) Which of these genotypes is heterozygous — FF, Ff or ff? ☑
17) Name one inherited disorder. ☑
18) Give one argument against screening embryos for inherited disorders. ☑

Variation, Evolution and Antibiotic-Resistant Bacteria (p.128-133) ☑
19) What is variation? ☑
20) Name the process by which evolution happens. ☑
21) What leads to the formation of antibiotic-resistant strains of bacteria? ☑

Selective Breeding and Genetic Engineering (p.135-137) ☑
22) What is selective breeding? ☑
23) What is genetic engineering? ☑

Fossils and Classification (p.139-141) ☑
24) What are fossils? ☑
25) What is the smallest group in the Linnaean system of classification? ☑

Competition

Organisms interact with each other and their environment. This is what ecology is all about.

Learn These Words Before You Start

1) Habitat — the place where an organism lives.
2) Population — all the organisms of one species in a habitat.
3) Community — all the populations of different species in a habitat.
4) Ecosystem — the interaction of a community of organisms with the non-living parts of their environment.

Organisms Compete for Resources to Survive

1) Resources are things that organisms need from their environment and other organisms to survive and reproduce:

- Animals need food, territory (space) and mates.
- Plants need light, water, space and mineral ions.

2) Organisms compete with other species (and members of their own species) for the same resources.

Organisms in a Community are Interdependent

1) In a community, different species depend on each other for things like food, shelter, pollination and seed dispersal. This is called interdependence.

2) This means that a big change in one part of an ecosystem (e.g. a species being removed) can affect the whole community.

3) The diagram on the right shows part of a food web (a diagram of what eats what) from a stream.

4) If all the stonefly larvae die, then for example:

- There would be less food for waterboatmen, so their population might decrease.
- The blackfly larvae would not have to compete with the stonefly larvae for food (algae) so their population might increase.

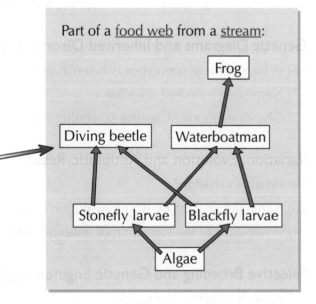

Part of a food web from a stream:

5) In stable communities, all the species and environmental factors are in balance. This means that the population sizes stay about the same.

Abiotic and Biotic Factors

The <u>environment</u> in which organisms live <u>changes</u> all the time. The <u>things that change</u> are either <u>abiotic</u> (non-living) or <u>biotic</u> (living) factors. These changes can have a big <u>effect</u> on a community...

Abiotic Factors Can **Change** in an **Ecosystem**

<u>Abiotic factors</u> are the <u>non-living</u> factors in an environment. For example:

1) <u>Moisture level</u>

2) <u>Light intensity</u>

3) <u>Temperature</u>

Light intensity can vary within an ecosystem because of shading caused by, e.g. tree cover.

4) <u>Carbon dioxide level</u> (for plants)

5) <u>Wind intensity</u> and <u>direction</u>

6) <u>Oxygen level</u> (for animals that live in water)

7) <u>Soil pH</u> and <u>mineral content</u>

Changes in Abiotic Factors Can **Affect Populations**

1) An <u>increase</u> or <u>decrease</u> in an abiotic factor is a <u>change</u> in the environment.

2) This can affect the <u>size</u> of <u>populations</u> in a <u>community</u>.

3) A change in an abiotic factor that affects one species could also affect the population sizes of <u>other</u> species that <u>depend on them</u> (see previous page). For example:

- A <u>decrease</u> in the <u>mineral content</u> of the soil could affect the <u>growth</u> of a plant species.
- This could cause a <u>decrease</u> in the <u>population size</u> of the plant species.
- A decrease in the plant population could <u>affect</u> any <u>animal species</u> that <u>depend</u> on it for <u>food</u>.

A = not, biotic = living, so abiotic means non-living

Some <u>human activities</u> can affect the <u>abiotic factors</u> of <u>ecosystems</u> — see pages 156, 159 and 160 for more.
As you can see from this page, this can affect some organisms <u>directly</u> and other organisms <u>indirectly</u>.

Abiotic and Biotic Factors

The previous page shows how abiotic factors can affect the <u>populations</u> in an ecosystem, but changes in <u>biotic factors</u> can also have big consequences. This page has a few examples to show you how.

Biotic Factors Can Also **Change** in an Ecosystem

1) <u>Biotic factors</u> are the <u>living</u> factors in an environment.
2) A change in a biotic factor could affect the <u>population size</u> of some species. This could then affect species that <u>depend</u> on them (see page 144).
3) Biotic factors include:

1. Competition

One species may <u>outcompete</u> another so that numbers are too low to breed.

> 'Outcompete' means they're better at getting the resources they need to survive.

- Red and grey <u>squirrels</u> live in the same habitat and eat the same food.
- Grey squirrels <u>outcompete</u> the red squirrels for food and shelter.
- So the <u>population</u> of red squirrels is <u>decreasing</u>.

2. **Availability** of **Food**

If there is <u>less food</u> available, the population size will <u>decrease</u>.

3. New Predators

<u>Predators</u> are animals that kill other animals

A new predator could cause a <u>decrease</u> in the <u>prey</u> population. There's more about predator-prey populations on page 148.

4. New Pathogens

<u>Pathogens</u> are microorganisms that cause disease.

A new pathogen could <u>quickly decrease</u> the population of an affected species.

Changing biotic factors — it's like dominoes...

<u>Learn</u> the list of factors here, as well as on the previous page. I reckon this is a prime time for shutting the book, <u>scribbling</u> them all down and then checking how you did.

Adaptations

Life exists in so many different environments. It's all because of the adaptations that organisms have...

Adaptations Allow Organisms to Survive

1) Organisms, including microorganisms, are adapted to survive in the conditions of their environment.
2) This means they have special features that suit their environment.
3) These features are called adaptations. Adaptations can be:

1. Structural

These are features of an organism's body structure — such as shape or colour. For example:

Animals that live in hot places (like camels) have a thin layer of fat and a large surface area compared to their volume. This helps them lose heat.

Arctic animals (like the Arctic fox) have white fur so they can't be seen against the snow. This helps them avoid predators and sneak up on prey.

2. Behavioural

These are ways that organisms behave.

E.g. many species (e.g. swallows) migrate (move away) to warmer climates during the winter. So they avoid the problems of living in cold conditions.

3. Functional

These are things that go on inside an organism's body.
They can be related to processes like metabolism (all the chemical reactions happening in the body).

E.g. desert animals make sure they don't lose too much water. They produce very little sweat and small amounts of concentrated urine (wee without much water in it).

Extremophiles Live in Extreme Places

Some microorganisms (e.g. bacteria) are extremophiles — they're adapted to live in extreme conditions. For example:

- at high temperatures (e.g. in super hot volcanic vents)
- in places with a high salt concentration (e.g. very salty lakes)
- at high pressure (e.g. in deep sea vents).

Organisms can adapt to life in really extreme environments

You might have to say how an organism is adapted to its environment. Look at its characteristics (e.g. colour) and the conditions it has to cope with (e.g. predation) and you'll be sorted.

Food Chains

You might remember <u>food webs</u> from page 144. Well, <u>food chains</u> are a similar idea — except that you only really show one part of a food web in a food chain. Read on to find out more...

Food Chains Show **What's Eaten by What**

1) <u>Food chains</u> always start with a <u>producer</u>.

2) Producers <u>make</u> (produce) <u>their own food</u> using energy from the Sun.

3) Producers are usually <u>green plants</u> or <u>algae</u> — they make <u>glucose</u> by <u>photosynthesis</u> (see page 87).

4) Some of this glucose is used to make the plant's <u>biomass</u> — its <u>mass</u> of <u>living material</u>.

5) Biomass is <u>passed along</u> a food chain when an organism <u>eats</u> another organism.

6) <u>Consumers</u> are organisms that <u>eat other organisms</u>:

- <u>Primary</u> consumers eat <u>producers</u>.
- <u>Secondary</u> consumers eat <u>primary</u> consumers.
- <u>Tertiary</u> consumers eat <u>secondary</u> consumers.

7) Here's an example of a <u>food chain</u>:

| Producers | Primary consumers | Secondary consumer |

Populations of **Prey** and **Predators** Go in **Cycles**

For more about a stable community see page 144.

1) Consumers that <u>hunt and kill</u> other animals are called <u>predators</u>.

2) The animals they eat are called <u>prey</u>.

3) In a <u>stable community</u>, the <u>population size</u> of a species is <u>limited</u> by the amount of <u>food</u> it has. So the population size of <u>predators</u> is <u>affected</u> by the number of their <u>prey</u>.

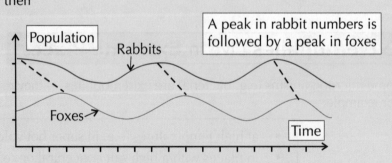

1) Foxes are <u>predators</u>. Rabbits are their <u>prey</u>.

2) If the <u>number of rabbits increases</u>, then the number of <u>foxes</u> will <u>increase</u>.

3) This is because there is <u>more food</u> for the foxes.

4) But as the number of foxes <u>increases</u>, then the number of rabbits will <u>decrease</u>.

5) This is because <u>more</u> rabbits will be <u>eaten</u> by the foxes.

A peak in rabbit numbers is followed by a peak in foxes

Population

Rabbits

Foxes

Time

4) It <u>takes a while</u> for one population to <u>respond</u> to changes in the other one.

E.g. the number of foxes goes up <u>after</u> the number of rabbits goes up. This is because it <u>takes time</u> for the foxes to <u>reproduce</u>.

Warm-Up & Exam Questions

This ecology topic's a long one — so make sure you've really got these first few pages stuck in your head before moving on and learning the rest. These questions should help you out.

Warm-Up Questions

1) Animals compete with one another for food. Give one other factor that animals compete for.
2) Name two abiotic factors.
3) True or false? Food chains always start with a primary consumer.
4) What would happen to the size of a predator population if there was less prey available?

Exam Questions

1 The Amazon rainforest is the biggest tropical rainforest in the world. **(Grade 3-4)**

1.1 The Amazon rainforest is a habitat for many different species. Describe what is meant by a habitat.

[1 mark]

1.2 Which word can be used to describe all the different species living in a habitat? Tick **one** box.

☐ population ☐ community ☐ ecosystem ☐ distribution

[1 mark]

2 **Figure 1** shows a food chain for a particular area: **(Grade 4-5)**

Figure 1

| algae → shrimp → sea turtle → tiger shark |

2.1 What term is used to describe the tiger shark in **Figure 1**? Tick **one** box.

☐ producer ☐ primary consumer ☐ secondary consumer ☐ tertiary consumer

[1 mark]

2.2 Explain the importance of the algae in **Figure 1**.

[2 marks]

3 **Figure 2** shows a penguin. Some of its adaptations are labelled. Penguins live in the cold, icy environment of the Antarctic. They swim in the sea to hunt for fish to eat. Some penguins also huddle together in large groups to keep warm. **(Grade 4-5)**

Figure 2

thick layer of fat
flippers
webbed feet

3.1 What type of adaptation is being described when penguins 'huddle together'?

[1 mark]

3.2 Use the labels on the diagram to explain **one** way that the penguin is adapted to its environment.

[2 marks]

Using Quadrats

This is where the <u>fun</u> starts. Studying <u>ecology</u> gives you the chance to <u>rummage around</u> in bushes, get your hands <u>dirty</u> and look at some <u>real organisms</u>, living in the wild.

Differences in the Environment Affect Where Organisms Live

1) The <u>distribution</u> of an organism is <u>where</u> an organism is <u>found</u>.

2) Where an organism is found is affected by <u>biotic and abiotic factors</u> (see pages 145-146).

3) An organism might be <u>more common</u> in <u>one area</u> than another due to <u>differences</u> in <u>factors</u> between the two areas. For example, in a field, you might find daisies are more common in the <u>open</u> than <u>under trees</u>, because there's <u>more light</u>.

4) To <u>study</u> the distribution of an organism you can use <u>quadrats</u> or <u>transects</u> (see next page).

Use Quadrats to Study The Distribution of Small Organisms

Here's how to compare <u>how common</u> an organism is in <u>two different areas</u> — these are called <u>sample areas</u>.

A quadrat (square frame)

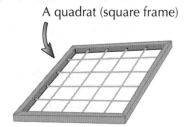

1) Place a <u>quadrat</u> on the ground in the <u>first</u> sample area. It needs to be placed at <u>random</u> (see p.171).

2) <u>Count</u> all the organisms you're interested in <u>within</u> the quadrat.

3) <u>Repeat</u> steps 1 and 2 as many times as you can.

4) <u>Work out</u> the <u>mean</u> number of organisms per quadrat within the first sample area.

 **Anna counted the number of daisies in 7 quadrats within her first sample area. She recorded the following results: 18, 20, 22, 23, 23, 23, 25**

Here the MEAN is: $\dfrac{\text{TOTAL number of organisms}}{\text{NUMBER of quadrats}} = \dfrac{154}{7} = 22$ daisies per quadrat

5) <u>Repeat</u> steps 1 to 4 in the <u>second</u> sample area.

6) Finally <u>compare</u> the two means. E.g. you might find 2 daisies per quadrat in a shady area, and 22 daisies per quadrat (lots more) in a sunny area.

You Can Work Out the Population Size of an Organism

The population size of an organism is sometimes called its abundance.

 **Students used quadrats, each with an area of 0.25 m², to randomly sample daisies in a field. They found a mean of 10 daisies per quadrat. The field's area was 800 m². Estimate the population of daisies in the field.**

1) Divide the area of the habitat by the quadrat size.

$800 \div 0.25 = 3200$

2) Multiply this by the mean number of organisms per quadrat.

$3200 \times 10 = 32\,000$ daisies in the field

Using Quadrats

So, now you think you've learnt all about distribution. Well hold on — there's more ecology fun to be had.

Use **Transects** to **Study** The **Distribution** of Organisms

You can use lines called transects to help find out how organisms are distributed across an area.
E.g. if an organism becomes more or less common as you move from a hedge towards the middle of a field.
Here's what to do:

1) Mark out a line in the area you want to study using a tape measure.

2) Collect data along the line by either:

   • Counting all the organisms you're interested in that touch the line.

   • Or by using quadrats (see previous page) placed along the line.

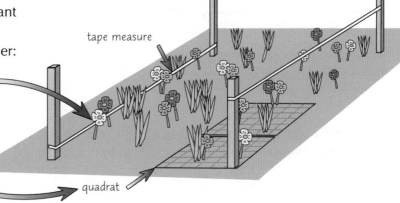

tape measure

quadrat

You Can **Estimate** the **Percentage Cover** of a **Quadrat**

1) Sometimes it can be difficult to count all of the organisms in a quadrat (e.g. if they're grass).

2) In this case, you can find the percentage cover instead.

3) This means estimating the percentage area of the quadrat that the organisms cover.

4) You can do this by counting the number of little squares they cover.

EXAMPLE: Some students were measuring the distribution of an organism across a school playing field. They placed quadrats at regular intervals along a transect.
Below is a picture of one of the quadrats.
Calculate the percentage cover of the organism in this quadrat.

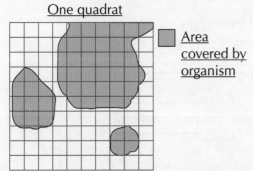

One quadrat

▨ Area covered by organism

1) Count the number of squares covered by the organism. You count a square if it's more than half covered.

   47 squares are covered by the organism.

2) Make this into a percentage:

   • Divide the number of squares covered by the organism by the total number of squares in the quadrat (100).

   • Multiply the result by 100.

   $(47/100) \times 100$
   $= 0.47 \times 100 = 47\%$

PRACTICAL TIP

You don't need fancy kit to study the distribution of organisms

So if you want to measure the distribution of a organism across an area, you could use a transect. You can use them alone or along with quadrats. Using percentage cover instead of number of organisms is a good way of studying the distribution of plants, as there may be too many to count.

The Water Cycle

The <u>amount</u> of water on Earth is pretty much <u>constant</u> — but <u>where</u> it is changes.
Water moves between <u>rivers</u>, <u>lakes</u>, <u>oceans</u> and the <u>atmosphere</u> in what's known as the <u>water cycle</u>.

The **Water Cycle** Means Water is **Constantly Recycled**

1) <u>Energy</u> from the <u>Sun</u> makes water <u>evaporate</u> from the land and sea. This turns the water into <u>water vapour</u>.

2) Water also evaporates from <u>plants</u> — this is called <u>transpiration</u> (see p.69).

3) The warm water vapour is <u>carried upwards</u>. When it gets higher up, the water vapour <u>cools</u>. It <u>condenses</u> to form <u>clouds</u>.

As warm water vapour rises it cools down and forms clouds.

4) Water falls from the clouds as <u>precipitation</u> (usually rain, but sometimes snow or hail). <u>Precipitation</u> provides <u>fresh water</u> for <u>plants</u> and <u>animals</u>:

Plants

1) Some water is <u>absorbed</u> by the <u>soil</u>.
Plants <u>take up</u> the water through their <u>roots</u>.

2) Plants <u>need</u> water for things like <u>photosynthesis</u> (p.87).

3) Some water becomes part of the plants' <u>tissues</u>.
It's passed to <u>animals</u> when plants are <u>eaten</u>.

Animals

1) Animals need water for the <u>chemical</u> reactions in their bodies.

2) They <u>return</u> water to the <u>soil</u> and <u>atmosphere</u> in their <u>waste</u> (e.g. sweat and urine).

5) Water that doesn't get absorbed by the soil will <u>run off</u> into <u>streams</u> and <u>rivers</u>.

6) The water <u>drains</u> back into the <u>sea</u>. Then it <u>evaporates</u> all over <u>again</u>.

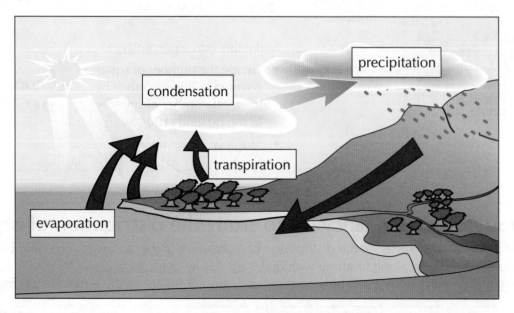

The Carbon Cycle

All the <u>nutrients</u> in our environment get <u>recycled</u> — there's a balance between what <u>goes in</u> and what <u>goes out</u>.

Materials are Recycled by Decay

1) <u>Living things</u> are made of <u>materials</u> they <u>take</u> from the world around them.

> E.g. plants take up <u>mineral ions</u> from the soil.
> * These are used to make <u>molecules</u> that make up the plant.
> * The molecules are <u>passed up the food chain</u> when the plant is <u>eaten</u>.

2) These materials are <u>returned</u> to the environment in <u>waste products</u>, or when <u>dead</u> organisms <u>decay</u>.

3) Materials decay because they're <u>broken down</u> by <u>microorganisms</u>.

4) <u>Decay</u> puts stuff that plants need to <u>grow</u> (e.g. mineral ions) <u>back</u> into the <u>soil</u> — they are <u>recycled</u>.

The Constant Cycling of Carbon is called the Carbon Cycle

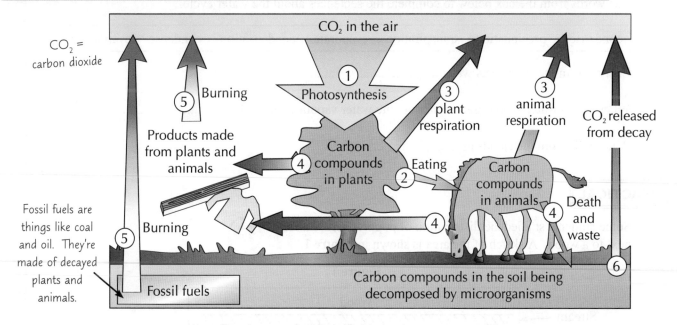

1. Plants take in CO_2 from the air during <u>photosynthesis</u>. They use the carbon in CO_2 to make <u>glucose</u>. This glucose is used to make carbon compounds, e.g. <u>carbohydrates</u>. These are used for <u>growth</u>.

2. <u>Eating</u> passes the carbon compounds in plants along to <u>animals</u> in the <u>food chain</u>.

3. Both plant and animal <u>respiration</u> releases CO_2 back into the <u>air</u>.

See p.93-94 for more on respiration.

4. Plants and animals eventually <u>die</u>, or are killed and turned into <u>useful products</u>.

5. <u>Burning</u> plant and animal products (and fossil fuels) releases CO_2 back into the air.

6. <u>Microorganisms</u> break down <u>animal waste</u> and <u>dead organisms</u>. As they break down the material, they <u>release CO_2</u> back into the air through <u>respiration</u>.

Warm-Up & Exam Questions

You can't just stare at these pages and expect all of the information to go in. Especially the practical pages with the maths examples. Do these questions to see how well you really know the stuff.

Warm-Up Questions

1) Give one piece of equipment that you could use to study the distribution of an organism.
2) Name one type of precipitation.
3) What is the role of microorganisms in the carbon cycle?
4) How is the carbon in fossil fuels returned to the atmosphere?

Exam Questions

1 The water cycle describes the constant movement of water molecules on the Earth.

Use words from the box below to complete the sentences about the water cycle.

| condenses | precipitation | transpiration | evaporate | condensation | condense | evaporates |

Energy from the sun makes water ....

When warm water vapour gets higher up, the water vapour cools and ....

Water falls from the clouds as ....

[3 marks]

PRACTICAL

2 Some students studied the distribution of poppies across a field next to a wood. A sketch of the area is shown in **Figure 1**.

Figure 1

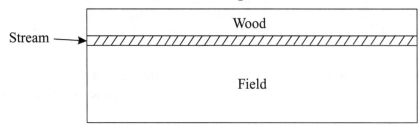

The students' results are shown in **Table 1**.

Table 1

Number of poppies per m²	5	9	14	19	26
Distance from wood (m)	2	4	6	8	10

2.1 Describe the trend shown in **Table 1**.

[1 mark]

2.2 The students suggest that light intensity may affect the distribution of the poppies.
Give **one** other factor that could affect the distribution of the poppies.

[1 mark]

Exam Questions

3   **Figure 2** shows a simplified version of the carbon cycle.

Figure 2

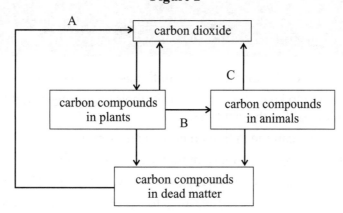

3.1   Name the process that is occurring at stage **B**.

[1 mark]

3.2   Name the process that is occurring at stage **C**.

[1 mark]

3.3   Explain how carbon is released from dead matter in the soil (stage **A**).

[2 marks]

3.4   Name the only process in the carbon cycle that removes carbon dioxide from the air.

[1 mark]

| PRACTICAL |

4   A group of students decided to study the distribution of a grass species in a field.
     Figure 3 shows a sketch of the grass species in one of their quadrats.

Figure 3

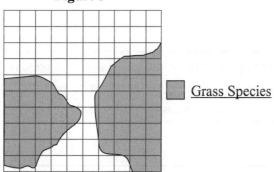

4.1   Use **Figure 3** to estimate the percentage cover of the grass species in the quadrat.

[1 mark]

4.2   Give **one** reason why the students may have decided to estimate the percentage cover of the grass.

[1 mark]

Biodiversity and Waste Management

Unfortunately, human activity can <u>negatively affect</u> the <u>planet</u> and its <u>variety of life</u>.

Earth's **Biodiversity** is Important

Biodiversity is the <u>variety of different species</u> of organisms on Earth, or within an ecosystem.

1) Different species <u>depend</u> on each other for different things in an ecosystem (see page 144).
2) Different species can also help keep the <u>conditions</u> in their <u>environment</u> right for each other, e.g. they can help keep the soil at the right pH.
3) So having a <u>high biodiversity</u> can mean that an ecosystem is more <u>stable</u>.
4) For the human species to <u>survive</u>, it's important that a good level of biodiversity is maintained.
5) Lots of human actions are <u>reducing</u> biodiversity (see below, and pages 158-160).
6) It's only <u>recently</u> that we've started <u>taking measures</u> to <u>stop</u> biodiversity decreasing.

More People Means Greater Demands on the **Environment**

1) The <u>population</u> of the world is <u>increasing</u> very quickly.
2) <u>More people</u> need <u>more resources</u> to survive.
3) People are also demanding a <u>higher standard of living</u>. This means that more people want <u>luxuries</u> that make life more comfortable, e.g. cars, computers, etc.
4) This means that we use <u>more raw materials</u> and <u>more energy</u> to make things.
5) So resources are being <u>used</u> more quickly than they are being <u>replaced</u>.

We're Also Producing **More Waste**

1) As we make more things, we produce more <u>waste</u>. This includes <u>waste chemicals</u>.
2) This waste can cause <u>harmful pollution</u> if it's not <u>handled properly</u>.
3) Pollution <u>kills</u> plants and animals. This <u>reduces biodiversity</u>.
4) <u>Pollution</u> can affect:

Water
- <u>Sewage</u> and <u>toxic chemicals</u> from industry can pollute lakes, rivers and oceans.
- <u>Fertilisers</u> (and other chemicals) used on land can be washed into water.
- This will affect the plants and animals that rely on these sources of water for survival.

Land
- We use <u>toxic chemicals</u> for farming (e.g. pesticides and herbicides).
- We dump a lot of <u>household waste</u> in landfill sites.

Air
- <u>Smoke</u> and <u>acidic gases</u> can pollute the air if they are released into the atmosphere.

Global Warming

You might remember the <u>carbon cycle</u> from p.153. Well, carbon dioxide has an important role in keeping the Earth <u>warm enough</u> for life. It's not so good when there's <u>too much</u> of it in the atmosphere though...

Carbon Dioxide and Methane Trap Energy from the Sun

1) Gases in the Earth's <u>atmosphere</u> trap energy from the Sun.

2) These gases mean that <u>not all</u> of the <u>energy</u> is <u>lost</u> into space. This helps to keep the Earth <u>warm</u>.

3) These gases are called <u>greenhouse gases</u>. Without them the Earth would be <u>very cold</u>.

4) But the levels of two greenhouse gases are <u>increasing</u> — <u>carbon dioxide</u> (CO_2) and <u>methane</u>.

5) The increasing <u>levels</u> of greenhouse gases are causing the Earth to <u>heat up</u> — this is <u>global warming</u>.

CO_2 and methane

Energy from the Sun

Energy trapped by gases

Global Warming

The Earth is getting <u>warmer</u>. Climate scientists are now trying to work out what the <u>effects</u> of global warming might be — sadly, it's not as simple as everyone having nicer summers.

The **Results** of **Global Warming** Could be Pretty **Serious**

There are several reasons to be <u>worried</u> about global warming. Here are a few:

Flooding

1) Higher temperatures cause <u>seawater</u> to <u>expand</u> and <u>ice</u> to <u>melt</u>. This causes the sea level to <u>rise</u>.
2) If it keeps rising it'll lead to <u>flooding</u> of low-lying land.
3) This will result in the loss of <u>habitats</u> (where organisms live).

Changes in the distribution of species

1) Global warming may lead to changes in <u>rainfall</u> and <u>temperature</u> in many areas.
2) This could cause the <u>distribution</u> (spread) of many <u>animal</u> and <u>plant species</u> to change.
3) E.g. if some areas become <u>warmer</u>:
   - Species that <u>do well</u> in <u>warm</u> conditions may spread <u>further</u>.
   - Species that need <u>cooler temperatures</u> may have a <u>smaller</u> area to live in.

Less biodiversity

1) Some species may not be able to <u>survive</u> a <u>change</u> in the climate.
2) These species might become <u>extinct</u>.
3) This could <u>reduce biodiversity</u> (see p.156).

Changes in migration patterns

1) There could be <u>changes in migration patterns</u> (where animals move to during different seasons).
2) E.g. some birds may migrate <u>further north</u>, as more northern areas are getting <u>warmer</u>.

WORKING SCIENTIFICALLY

We need to act fast, before the worst effects of climate change

Global warming is rarely out of the news. <u>Most scientists</u> accept that it's happening and that <u>human activity</u> has caused most of the recent warming, based on the evidence that has so far been collected. However, they don't know exactly what the <u>effects</u> will be and scientists will have to collect more data before these questions can really be answered.

Deforestation and Land Use

Trees and peat bogs trap carbon dioxide and lock it up. The problems start when it escapes...

Humans Use Lots of Land for Lots of Purposes

1) We use land for things like building, quarrying, farming and dumping waste.
2) This means that there's less land available for other organisms.
3) Sometimes, the way we use land has a bad effect on the environment.

Destroying Peat Bogs Adds More CO_2 to the Atmosphere

1) Bogs are areas of land that are acidic and waterlogged.

2) Plants that live in bogs don't fully decay when they die. The partly-rotted plants build up to form peat.

3) So the carbon in the plants is stored in the peat.

4) Peat bogs can be drained, so the peat can be sold to gardeners as compost.

5) When the peat is drained, microorganisms can break it down. They release carbon dioxide (CO_2) when they respire.

6) Peat can also be sold as a fuel. CO_2 is released when the peat is burned.

7) Destroying the bogs reduces the area of the habitat.

8) This reduces the number of animals, plants and microorganisms that live there. So it reduces biodiversity.

We need to use land, but we also need a healthy environment

We can't really avoid using land — we need it to grow enough food or build enough houses for people. The human population is increasing so it's likely that we'll use even more land in the future. We'll have to find a way to manage land use to reduce the negative effects on the environment.

Deforestation and Land Use

Many parts of the world have <u>already</u> been changed lots by deforestation. For example, much of the <u>UK</u> used to be covered in forests. Deforestation can be <u>bad news</u> for several reasons.

Deforestation Means **Chopping Down Trees**

<u>Deforestation</u> is the <u>cutting down</u> of <u>forests</u>. It is done for many <u>reasons</u>, like:

- To <u>clear land</u> for farming (e.g. cattle or rice crops) to provide <u>more food</u>.
- To grow <u>crops</u> to make <u>biofuels</u>.

Deforestation Can Cause Many **Problems**

Deforestation causes big problems when it's done on a <u>large-scale</u>, e.g. cutting down rainforests in <u>tropical areas</u>. These are:

Less carbon dioxide taken in

- Trees take in carbon dioxide from the atmosphere during <u>photosynthesis</u> (page 87).
- So <u>cutting down</u> trees means that less carbon dioxide is <u>removed</u> from the atmosphere.
- Trees '<u>lock up</u>' some of the <u>carbon</u> in their wood. Removing trees means that less is locked up.

More carbon dioxide released

- Carbon dioxide is <u>released</u> when trees are <u>burnt</u> to clear land.
- <u>Microorganisms</u> feeding on <u>dead wood</u> release carbon dioxide through <u>respiration</u> (p.93).

More CO_2 in the atmosphere causes global warming (see p.157).

Less biodiversity

- Habitats like forests can contain many species of <u>plants</u> and <u>animals</u> — they have <u>high biodiversity</u>.
- When forests are destroyed, many species may become <u>extinct</u> (p.131). This <u>reduces</u> biodiversity.

Not a very cheerful page, I know...

Make sure you can link together all the information on pages 157-160 — for example, how <u>deforestation</u> and <u>peat burning</u> can contribute to <u>global warming</u>, and how this might affect <u>biodiversity</u>. In the exam, you might get an extended response question that requires you to draw on several different areas of knowledge like this.

Maintaining Ecosystems and Biodiversity

It's really important that biodiversity is <u>maintained</u> as damage to ecosystems or populations of species can be <u>hard to undo</u>. This page is about some of the different <u>methods</u> that can be used to maintain biodiversity.

There are **Programmes** to **Protect Ecosystems** and **Biodiversity**

1) Human activities can <u>reduce biodiversity</u> and <u>damage ecosystems</u>.

2) In some areas, <u>programmes</u> to <u>minimise the damage</u> have been set up by <u>concerned citizens</u> and <u>scientists</u>. Here are a few examples:

1. Breeding Programmes

1) Animal species that are at <u>risk</u> of dying out are called <u>endangered species</u>.

2) They can be bred in <u>captivity</u>.

3) This makes sure some individuals will <u>survive</u> if the species <u>dies out</u> in the wild.

4) Individuals can sometimes be <u>released</u> into the <u>wild</u>. This can be to <u>boost</u> a population or <u>replace</u> one that's been wiped out.

Pandas are an endangered species. Many efforts have been made to breed pandas in captivity.

2. Habitat Protection

<u>Protecting</u> and <u>regenerating</u> (rebuilding) <u>rare habitats</u> helps to protect the <u>species</u> that live there.

3. Reintroducing **Hedgerows** and **Field Margins**

1) Field margins are areas of land around the <u>edges</u> of fields where wild flowers and grasses are left to <u>grow</u>.

2) <u>Hedges</u> can be planted around fields to form <u>hedgerows</u>.

3) Hedgerows and field margins provide a <u>habitat</u> for <u>lots of types</u> of organisms.

4) This is very useful for fields that only have <u>one type of crop</u>. This is because these fields have <u>very low biodiversity</u>.

4. Recycling

1) This <u>reduces</u> the amount of <u>waste</u> that gets dumped in <u>landfill</u> sites.

2) This could <u>reduce</u> the amount of <u>land</u> taken over for landfill. So <u>ecosystems</u> can be left alone.

5. Government Programmes

1) Deforestation <u>increases</u> the amount of <u>carbon dioxide</u> in the atmosphere (see previous page).

2) Some governments have made <u>rules</u> to <u>reduce deforestation</u>.

3) They have also made rules to reduce the amount of <u>carbon dioxide</u> released by <u>businesses</u>.

4) This could help to <u>stop global warming increasing</u> (see page 157).

Warm-Up & Exam Questions

I hope you've got all of that important information in your head. There's a lot to remember here, so have a flick back when you're doing these questions in case you've forgotten any little details.

Warm-Up Questions

1) What is meant by 'biodiversity'?
2) Give one way in which land can become polluted.
3) Give two greenhouse gases.
4) True or false? Destroying peat bogs adds more CO_2 to the atmosphere.
5) What is meant by the term 'deforestation'?

Exam Questions

1   Ecosystems and biodiversity can be protected by programmes set up by scientists.

1.1   Hedgerows can be reintroduced around fields in order to protect biodiversity.

Give **one** reason why reintroducing hedgerows around fields is important for biodiversity.

[1 mark]

1.2   Breeding programmes can be used to protect endangered species.

Explain how breeding programmes can be used to prevent an endangered species from dying out.

[3 marks]

2   Humans are producing increasing amounts of waste.
This has negative impacts for biodiversity and the environment.

2.1   Give **two** types of waste that pollute the air.

[2 marks]

2.2   Describe **one** way in which waste produced by humans pollutes water.

[1 mark]

2.3   Give **two** reasons why humans are producing increasingly more waste.

[2 marks]

2.4   Recycling reduces the amount of waste that gets dumped at landfill sites.
Explain how this helps to protect biodiversity.

[1 mark]

3*   Most scientists accept that global warming is happening.
They believe that it could cause major changes to our environment.

Explain why deforestation contributes to global warming.

[6 marks]

Revision Summary for Topic 7

That's <u>Topic 7</u> done with. I bet you're in the mood for a long list of revision questions now. You're in luck.

* Try these questions and <u>tick off each one</u> when you <u>get it right</u>.
* When you've done <u>all the questions</u> under a heading and are <u>completely happy</u> with it, tick it off.

Competition, Abiotic and Biotic Factors, and Adaptations (p.144-147) ☑

1) Define 'ecosystem'.
2) What things do plants compete for in an ecosystem?
3) Explain what is meant by a 'stable community'.
4) What are biotic factors?
5) What are functional adaptations?

Food Chains, Quadrats and Transects (p.148-151) ☑

6) What do primary consumers eat?
7) What is meant by the term 'biomass'?
8) Explain how a quadrat can be used to investigate the distribution of clover plants in two areas.
9) Suggest why you might use a transect when investigating the distribution of organisms.

The Water and Carbon Cycles (p.152-153) ☑

10) When water vapour cools and condenses in the atmosphere, what does it change into?
11) What role do plants have in the carbon cycle?

Human Impacts on the Planet (p.156-161) ☑

12) Suggest why it's important to have high biodiversity in an ecosystem.
13) Give one way global warming could reduce biodiversity.
14) Explain why the destruction of peat bogs adds more carbon dioxide to the atmosphere.
15) Give two reasons why deforestation increases the amount of carbon dioxide in the atmosphere.
16) Why can field margins increase biodiversity?

Measuring Techniques

Get your lab coats on, it's time to find out about the skills you'll need in <u>experiments</u>...
First things first — make sure you're using <u>appropriate equipment</u> and know <u>how to use</u> it correctly.

Use the **Right Apparatus** to Take **Readings**

1. Mass

1) To measure mass, put the <u>container</u> you're measuring the substance <u>into</u> on the <u>balance</u>.
2) Set the balance to exactly <u>zero</u>. Then <u>add</u> your substance and <u>read off</u> the <u>mass</u>.

2. Temperature

1) Make sure the <u>bulb</u> of your thermometer is <u>completely under the surface</u> of the substance.
2) If you're taking a <u>starting temperature</u>, you should wait for the temperature to <u>stop changing</u>.
3) Read your measurement off the <u>scale</u> at <u>eye level</u>.

3. **Volume** of a **Liquid**

1) There are a few methods you might use to transfer a volume of liquid:

<u>Using a pipette</u>
1) <u>Dropping pipette</u> — Use this if you only want a <u>couple of drops</u> of liquid. It's also used if you <u>don't</u> need an <u>accurate volume</u> of liquid.
2) <u>Pipette</u> — Use this if you want an <u>accurate</u> volume of liquid. The <u>pipette filler</u> lets you <u>safely control</u> the amount of liquid you're drawing up.

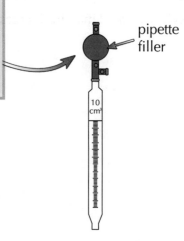

pipette filler

<u>Using a measuring cylinder</u>
These come in many different <u>sizes</u>. You need to use one that's the <u>right size</u> for the measurement you want to make (you don't want one that's <u>too big</u>).

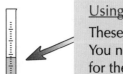

2) To measure the volume of a liquid, read the volume from the <u>bottom</u> of the <u>meniscus</u> (the curved upper surface of the liquid) when it's at <u>eye level</u>.

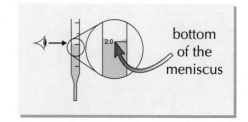

bottom of the meniscus

Measuring Techniques

4. **Volume** of a **Gas**

There are a few ways you can measure the volume of a gas:

1) Gas syringe — this is the most accurate way to measure gas volume.
   - Make sure the gas syringe is the right size for your measurements.
   - Make sure the plunger moves smoothly.
   - Read the volume from the scale on the syringe.

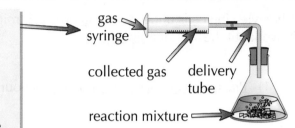

gas syringe

collected gas   delivery tube

reaction mixture

2) Upturned measuring cylinder filled with water.

3) Counting the bubbles produced or measuring the length of a gas bubble drawn along a tube (see page 90).
   - These methods are less accurate.
   - But they will give you results that you can compare.

Always make sure your equipment is sealed so no gas can escape. This will make your results more accurate.

5. pH

1) Indicator solutions can be used to estimate pH. Add a couple of drops of the indicator to the solution you want to test. It will change colour depending on if it's in an acid or an alkali.

2) There are also paper indicators. These are strips of paper that contain indicator. If you spot some solution onto indicator paper, the paper will change colour to show the pH. Indicator paper is useful when:
   - You don't want to change the colour of all of the substance.
   - The substance is already coloured (so it might hide the colour of the indicator).
   - You want to find the pH of a gas — hold a piece of damp indicator paper in a gas sample.

Litmus paper turns red in acidic conditions and blue in alkaline conditions.
Universal indicator paper can be used to estimate the pH based on its colour.

litmus paper

3) pH probes measure pH electronically. They are more accurate than indicators.

PRACTICAL TIP

Read off the scale carefully when taking readings

Whether you're reading off a thermometer, a pipette or a measuring cylinder, make sure you take all readings at eye level. And, if it's volume you're measuring, read from the bottom of the meniscus.

Measuring Cell Size

Next up, how to <u>measure</u> the <u>size</u> of a <u>single cell</u>, using your <u>microscope</u> and a ruler...

You Can **Measure** the **Size** of a **Single Cell**

When viewing <u>cells</u> under a <u>microscope</u>, you might need to work out their <u>size</u>. To work out the size of a <u>single cell</u>:

1) Place a <u>clear, plastic ruler</u> on <u>top</u> of your microscope <u>slide</u>.

You can read all about using a microscope on pages 19-20.

2) <u>Clip</u> the <u>ruler</u> and <u>slide</u> onto the <u>stage</u>.

3) Select the <u>objective lens</u> that gives an overall magnification of <u>x 100</u>.

4) Use the <u>coarse adjustment knob</u> and the <u>fine adjustment knob</u> to see a <u>clear image</u> of the cells.

5) <u>Move</u> the ruler so that the cells are <u>lined up</u> along <u>1 mm</u>.

6) <u>Count</u> the <u>number of cells</u> along this <u>1 mm sample</u>.

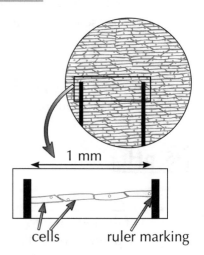

1 mm

cells   ruler marking

7) <u>1 mm = 1000 µm</u>. So you can <u>calculate</u> the <u>size</u> of a <u>single cell</u> using this <u>formula</u>:

$$\text{length of cell (µm)} = \frac{1000 \text{ µm}}{\text{number of cells counted in sample}}$$

EXAMPLE:

Under a microscope, 4 cells were counted in 1 mm.
Calculate the size of one cell. Give your answer in µm.

1 mm is the <u>same</u> as 1000 µm, so you just need to put the <u>number of cells</u> into the formula.

$$\text{length of cell (µm)} = \frac{1000 \text{ µm}}{4} = 250 \text{ µm}$$

Measuring Transpiration Rate

Moving on, it's time to take a look at how to use a <u>potometer</u> to calculate <u>transpiration rate</u>...

Set Up a **Potometer** to **Measure Transpiration Rate**

1) A <u>potometer</u> is a special piece of equipment.

2) You set it up as shown in the diagram.

3) You can use a <u>potometer</u> to <u>estimate</u> <u>transpiration rate</u> (see page 72).

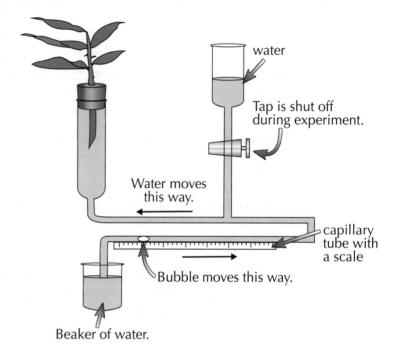

water

Tap is shut off during experiment.

Water moves this way.

capillary tube with a scale

Bubble moves this way.

Beaker of water.

Here's what you do:

1) Record the <u>starting position</u> of the <u>air bubble</u>.

2) Start a <u>stopwatch</u>.

3) As the plant takes up water, the air bubble gets <u>sucked</u> along the tube.

4) Record <u>how far</u> the air bubble moves in a <u>set time</u>.

5) Then you can <u>estimate</u> the <u>transpiration rate</u>.

EXAMPLE: **A potometer was used to estimate the transpiration rate of a plant cutting. The bubble moved 25 mm in 10 minutes. Estimate the transpiration rate.**

To estimate the <u>transpiration rate</u>, divide the <u>distance</u> the bubble moved by the <u>time taken</u>.

$$\text{Transpiration rate} = \frac{\text{distance bubble moved}}{\text{time taken}} = \frac{25 \text{ mm}}{10 \text{ min}}$$

$$= 2.5 \text{ mm/min}$$

 EXAM TIP

Working out rate always involves dividing by time

If you remember this, and can <u>pick out</u> the <u>right numbers</u> from the <u>question</u>, there's not much that can go wrong. Just make sure you <u>double-check</u> your calculation in the exam.

Safety and Ethics

There's <u>danger</u> all around, particularly in science experiments. But don't let this put you off. Just be aware of the <u>hazards</u> and take <u>sensible precautions</u>. Read on to find out more...

To Make Sure You're **Working Safely** in the **Lab** You Need to...

1) Wear <u>sensible clothing</u> (e.g. shoes that will protect your feet from spillages). Also, wear a <u>lab coat</u> to protect your <u>skin</u> and <u>clothing</u>.

2) Wear <u>safety goggles</u> to protect your <u>eyes</u>, and <u>gloves</u> to protect your <u>hands</u>.

3) Be aware of <u>general safety</u> in the lab. E.g. don't touch any <u>hot equipment</u>.

4) Follow any <u>instructions</u> that your teacher gives you <u>carefully</u>.

5) <u>Chemicals</u> and <u>equipment</u> can be <u>hazardous</u> (dangerous). E.g. some chemicals are <u>flammable</u> (they <u>catch fire easily</u>) — this means you must be careful <u>not</u> to use a <u>Bunsen burner</u> near them.

You Need to Think About **Ethical Issues**

Any <u>organisms</u> that you use in your experiments need to be treated <u>safely</u> and <u>ethically</u>. This means:

1) Animals should be <u>handled carefully</u>.

2) Any captured <u>wild animals</u> should be <u>returned to their habitat</u> after the experiment.

3) Any animals <u>kept</u> in the <u>lab</u> should be <u>well cared for</u>. E.g. they should have <u>plenty of space</u>.

4) Other <u>students</u> that <u>take part</u> in any experiment should be <u>happy</u> to do so.

BEWARE — hazardous biology experiments about...

<u>Before</u> you carry out an experiment, you must <u>consider all of the hazards</u>. They can be anything from <u>chemicals</u> to <u>sharp objects</u>, <u>pathogens</u> to <u>heating equipment</u>. Whatever the hazard, make sure you know all the <u>safety precautions</u> you should follow to keep yourself, and others, safe.

Heating Substances

Some more useful lab stuff for you now — a bit about <u>heating things up</u>.

Bunsen Burners **Heat** Things **Quickly**

Here's how to <u>use</u> a Bunsen burner...

1) Connect the Bunsen burner to a <u>gas tap</u>. Check that the <u>hole</u> is <u>closed</u>.

2) Place the Bunsen burner on a <u>heat-proof mat</u>.

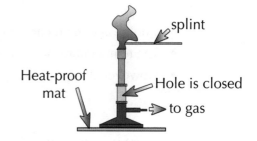

3) Light a <u>splint</u> and hold it over the Bunsen burner.

4) Now, <u>turn on</u> the gas. The Bunsen burner should light with a <u>yellow flame</u>.

5) <u>Open</u> the <u>hole</u> to turn the flame <u>blue</u>.
   The <u>more open</u> the hole, the <u>hotter</u> the flame.

6) Heat things <u>just above</u> the <u>blue cone</u> — this is the <u>hottest</u> part of the flame.

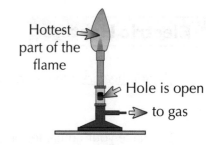

7) If you're heating a container (with your substance in it) <u>in</u> the flame, hold it at the <u>top</u> with a pair of <u>tongs</u>.

8) If you're heating a container <u>over</u> the flame, put a <u>tripod and gauze</u> over the Bunsen burner before you light it. Then place the container on the gauze.

Bunsen burners are useful, but need to be used in the right way

When the Bunsen burner <u>isn't heating</u> anything, it's important to <u>close the hole</u>. This turns the flame <u>yellow</u> — that flame isn't as hot and is much <u>easier to spot</u>, so it helps to prevent any burns...

Heating Substances

You need to be able to decide on the <u>best</u> and <u>safest</u> method for heating a substance...

Water Baths and Electric Heaters Have Set Temperatures

Water Baths

1) A <u>water bath</u> is a <u>container</u> filled with <u>water</u>. It can be heated to a <u>specific temperature</u>.

2) A <u>simple</u> water bath can be made by heating a <u>beaker of water</u> over a <u>Bunsen burner</u>.
   - The temperature is checked with a <u>thermometer</u>.
   - However, it's <u>hard</u> to keep the temperature of the water <u>constant</u>.

3) An <u>electric water bath</u> will <u>check</u> and <u>change</u> the temperature for you. Here's how you use one:

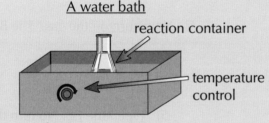

1) <u>Set</u> the <u>temperature</u> on the water bath.
2) Allow the water to <u>heat up</u>.
3) Place your container (with your substance in it) in the water bath using <u>tongs</u>.
4) The level of the water <u>outside</u> the container should be <u>just above</u> the level of the substance <u>inside</u> it.
5) The substance will be warmed to the <u>same temperature</u> as the water.

A water bath — reaction container — temperature control

4) The substance in the container is surrounded by water, so the heating is very <u>even</u>.

Electric Heaters

<u>Electric heaters</u> often have a metal <u>plate</u> that can be heated to a <u>specific temperature</u>.

1) Place your container on <u>top</u> of the <u>hot plate</u>.
2) You can heat substances to <u>higher temperatures</u> than you can in a water bath. (You <u>can't</u> use a water bath to heat something higher than <u>100 °C</u>.)
3) You have to <u>stir</u> the substance to make sure it's <u>heated evenly</u>.

Electric water baths are great for keeping the temperature constant

Make sure you're clear on how to use <u>electric water baths</u> and <u>heaters</u>, and more importantly, on how to use them <u>safely</u>. Obviously hot things are <u>very dangerous</u>, so <u>take care</u> — a trip to hospital would be no fun.

Sampling

You need to be able to carry out <u>sampling</u> that'll give you <u>non-biased results</u>. First up why, then how...

Sampling Should be **Random**

1) When you're investigating a <u>population</u>, it's usually <u>not possible</u> to study <u>every single organism</u> in it.

2) This means that you need to take <u>samples</u> of the population.

3) The samples need to <u>accurately</u> represent the <u>whole population</u>. This is so you can use them to <u>draw conclusions</u> about the <u>whole population</u>.

4) To make sure a sample represents the population, it should be <u>random</u>.

Organisms Should Be Sampled At **Random Sites** in an Area

1) <u>Quadrats</u> can be used to take <u>population samples</u> of an organism in an area (see page 161).

2) If you're looking at plant species in a field...

1) <u>Divide</u> the field into a <u>grid</u>.

2) <u>Label the grid</u> along the bottom and up the side with numbers.

3) Use a <u>random number generator</u> (e.g. on a computer or calculator) to select coordinates, e.g. (2,7).

4) Place your quadrats at these coordinates to take your <u>samples</u>.

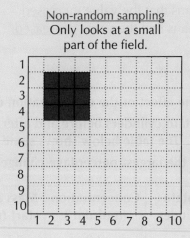

Non-random sampling
Only looks at a small part of the field.

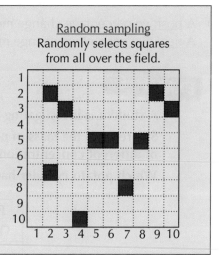

Random sampling
Randomly selects squares from all over the field.

Health Data Should be Taken from **Randomly Selected People**

You need to use <u>random sampling</u> to choose members of the population you're interested in.

E.g. a scientist is looking at health data in country X. She wants to know <u>how many</u> people in the country have both <u>Type 2 diabetes</u> and <u>heart disease</u>:

1) <u>Hospital records</u> show that <u>270 196</u> people in the country have Type 2 diabetes.

2) These people are given a <u>number</u> between 1 and 270 196.

3) A <u>random number generator</u> is used to choose the <u>sample group</u> — e.g. it selects individuals with the numbers 72 063, 11 822, 193 123, etc.

4) The records of the sample group are used to find the number of people with <u>heart disease</u> in it.

5) The <u>proportion</u> of people in the <u>sample group</u> who have heart disease is worked out.

6) This can be used to <u>estimate</u> the <u>total number</u> of people with Type 2 diabetes who also have heart disease.

Comparing Results

Once you've had fun collecting all your data, a few <u>calculations</u> might be needed to work out what your data actually shows. Calculating <u>percentage change</u> is a great way to <u>compare results</u>...

Percentage Change Allows you to Compare Results

1) When investigating the <u>change</u> in a variable, you may want to <u>compare</u> results that didn't have the <u>same starting value</u>.

> - For example, you may want to compare the <u>change in mass</u> of <u>potato cylinders</u> left in different concentrations of <u>sugar solution</u> (see page 31).
> - The cylinders probably all had <u>different masses</u> to <u>start with</u>.

2) To do this you can calculate the <u>percentage change</u>. You work it out like this:

$$\text{percentage (\%) change} = \frac{\text{final value} - \text{original value}}{\text{original value}} \times 100$$

3) A <u>positive</u> percentage change means that the value <u>increased</u>.
A <u>negative</u> percentage change means that the value <u>decreased</u>.

EXAMPLE:

A student is investigating the effect of the concentration of sugar solution on potato cells.

She records the mass of potato cylinders before and after placing them in sugar solutions of different concentrations. The table below shows some of her results.

Which potato cylinder had the largest percentage change?

Potato cylinder	Concentration (mol/dm³)	Mass at start (g)	Mass at end (g)
1	0.0	7.5	8.7
2	1.0	8.0	6.8

1) Stick each set of results into the <u>equation</u>: $\dfrac{\%}{\text{change}} = \dfrac{\text{final value} - \text{original value}}{\text{original value}} \times 100$

The mass at the <u>end</u> is the <u>final value</u>.

The mass at the <u>start</u> is the <u>original value</u>.

Here, the mass has <u>decreased</u> so the percentage change is <u>negative</u>.

potato cylinder 1: $\dfrac{8.7 - 7.5}{7.5} \times 100 = 16\%$ potato cylinder 2: $\dfrac{6.8 - 8.0}{8.0} \times 100 = -15\%$

2) <u>Compare</u> the results.   16% is greater than 15%. So potato cylinder 1 (in the 0.0 mol/dm³ sugar solution) had the largest percentage change.

Good practical skills are needed when you're doing an investigation...

...but you also need to know about them for your <u>exams</u>. You're guaranteed to be tested on your <u>practical knowledge</u>, so if you've merrily skipped through this section, you'd better <u>go back</u> and <u>read it through again</u>.

Practice Exams

Once you've been through all the questions in this book, you should feel pretty confident about the exams. As final preparation, here is a set of **practice exams** to really get you set for the real thing. The time allowed for each paper is 1 hour 15 minutes. These papers are designed to give you the best possible preparation for your exams.

CGP   Practice Exam Paper
GCSE Combined Science

GCSE Combined Science

Biology Paper 1

Foundation Tier

In addition to this paper you should have:
• A ruler.
• A calculator.

Centre name				
Centre number				
Candidate number				

Time allowed:
• 1 hour 15 minutes

Surname	
Other names	
Candidate signature	

Instructions to candidates
• Write your name and other details in the spaces provided above.
• Answer **all** questions in the spaces provided.
• Do all rough work on the paper.
• Cross out any work you do not want to be marked.

Information for candidates
• The marks available are given in brackets at the end of each question.
• There are 70 marks available for this paper.
• You are allowed to use a calculator.
• You should use good English and present your answers in a clear and organised way.
• For Questions 6.5 and 7.2 ensure that your answers have a clear and logical structure, include the right scientific terms, spelt correctly and include detailed, relevant information.

Advice to candidates
• In calculations show clearly how you worked out your answers.

For examiner's use

Q	Attempt Nº			Q	Attempt Nº		
	1	2	3		1	2	3
1				5			
2				6			
3				7			
4				8			
Total							

1   **Figure 1** shows the human respiratory system.

Figure 1

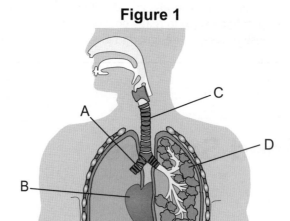

1.1   Which of the labels on **Figure 1** points to the trachea?
Tick **one** box.

☐ A   ☐ B   ☐ C   ☐ D

[1 mark]

1.2   Which of the labels on **Figure 1** shows where gas exchange takes place?
Tick **one** box.

☐ A   ☐ B   ☐ C   ☐ D

[1 mark]

1.3   Cells in the human body are organised into different levels.

Draw **one** line from each description of a level of cell organisation to
the example of that level.

A group of similar cells that work together to carry out a function		Lungs
A group of organs working together to perform a function		Epithelial tissue
A group of different tissues that work together to perform a certain function		Respiratory system

[2 marks]

1.4 An athlete ran on a treadmill for 11 minutes. In that time she took 407 breaths.

What was the athlete's average breathing rate in breaths per minute?
Tick **one** box.

☐ 24   ☐ 37   ☐ 48   ☐ 61

[1 mark]

1.5 **Figure 2** shows an alveolus and a blood capillary.

Figure 2

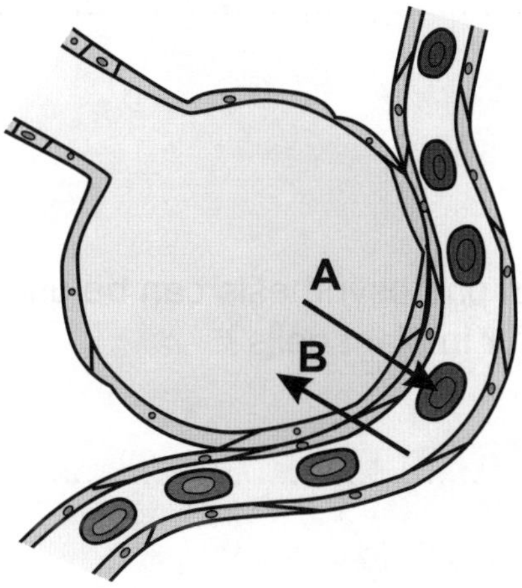

The arrows on the diagram show the net movement of two gases, **A** and **B**.
Name gases **A** and **B**.

Gas **A**: ....

Gas **B**: ....

[2 marks]

Turn over for the next question

2   Plants produce glucose during photosynthesis.

2.1   Complete the word equation for photosynthesis.

carbon dioxide + water ⟶ glucose + ...

[1 mark]

2.2   Name the subcellular structure that absorbs light for photosynthesis.

....

[1 mark]

2.3   The glucose produced in photosynthesis can be used by plants to make cellulose.
What is cellulose used for in plant cells?

....

[1 mark]

2.4   Use a word from the box to complete the sentence below.

damaged	reproduced	respired	differentiated

Plants kept in a greenhouse that has become too hot may stop photosynthesising.

This is because the enzymes needed for photosynthesis are ....

[1 mark]

A student is investigating the effect of light intensity on the rate of photosynthesis. **Figure 3** shows the apparatus. **Table 1** shows the student's results.

Figure 3

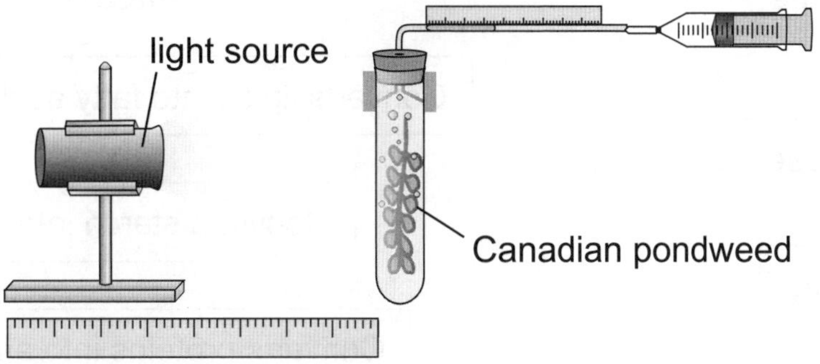

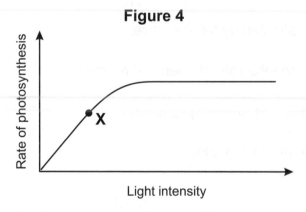

light source

Canadian pondweed

Table 1

Relative light intensity	1	2	3	4	5	6	7	8	9	10
Volume of gas produced in 10 minutes (cm³)	8	12	18	25	31	13	42	48	56	61

2.5   At which relative light intensity did the student record an anomalous result?

....

[1 mark]

2.6   The student plotted a graph of the rate of photosynthesis against relative light intensity. **Figure 4** shows the student's graph.

Figure 4

Rate of photosynthesis

X

Light intensity

At point **X**, what is the limiting factor of photosynthesis?
Tick **one** box.

☐   oxygen concentration

☐   temperature

☐   light intensity

☐   carbon dioxide concentration

[1 mark]

Turn over for the next question

Turn over ▶

3   There are a number of digestive enzymes found in the human body.

3.1   Draw **one** line from each digestive enzyme to its function.

Enzyme   Function

Converts lipids into fatty acids and glycerol

Protease

Converts starch into sugars

Lipase

Converts proteins into amino acids

[2 marks]

3.2   Explain why different enzymes catalyse different reactions.

....

....

....
[2 marks]

3.3   Which of the following statements about enzymes is **not** true?
Tick **one** box.

☐   Enzymes are affected by temperature.

☐   Enzymes change the rate of chemical reactions.

☐   Enzymes are changed during reactions.

☐   Enzymes are affected by pH.

[1 mark]

3.4   Explain why reactions catalysed by amylase are important for growth.
Your answer should refer to respiration.

....

....

....

....
[3 marks]

4   **Figure 5** shows the rate of transpiration in two plants over 48 hours.

Figure 5

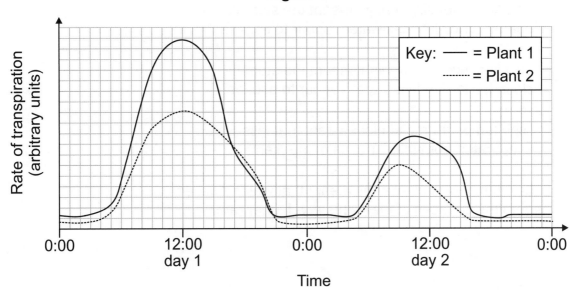

4.1   Define the term transpiration.

....

[1 mark]

4.2   At what time on **day 2** was the rate of transpiration highest for **plant 2**?

....

[1 mark]

4.3   The rate of transpiration for both plants was slower on **day 2** than on **day 1**.
Suggest **one** reason for this.

....

....

[1 mark]

Question 4 continues on the next page

Turn over ▶

4.4 Why was the rate of transpiration for both plants very low at night?
Tick **one** box.

☐ Low light intensity at night meant the stomata
opened, allowing less water vapour to escape.

☐ Low light intensity at night meant the stomata
closed, allowing less water vapour to escape.

☐ High temperatures at night meant that less water
evaporated from the surfaces of the plants.

☐ Low temperatures at night meant that water diffused
from the surfaces of the plants at a higher rate.

[1 mark]

Figure 6 shows two stomata on the surface of a leaf viewed under a microscope.

Figure 6

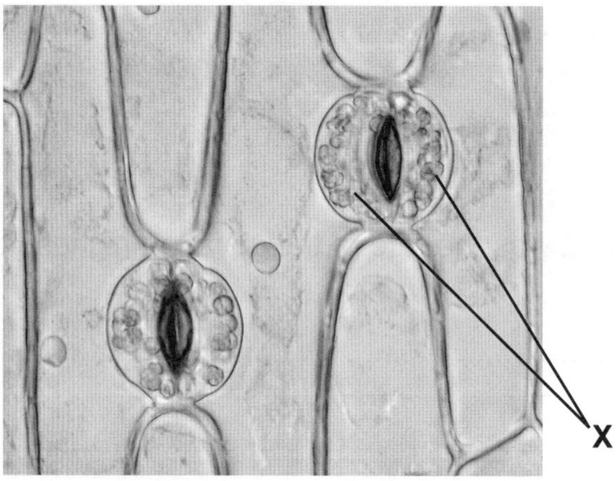

© MAREK MIS/SCIENCE PHOTO LIBRARY

4.5 Name the cells labelled **X**.

....
[1 mark]

5 A student investigated how well stem cells from a plant grew in four different growth media.

The student placed a block of stem tissue measuring 1 mm × 1 mm × 1 mm onto each growth medium. They were then incubated at 35 °C for two days.

At the end of that time, the blocks were taken out and weighed to see how much they had grown. **Table 2** shows the student's results.

Table 2

Growth medium	% increase in mass
1	120
2	85
3	65
4	90

5.1 Use the results from **Table 2** to complete the bar chart in **Figure 7**.

Figure 7

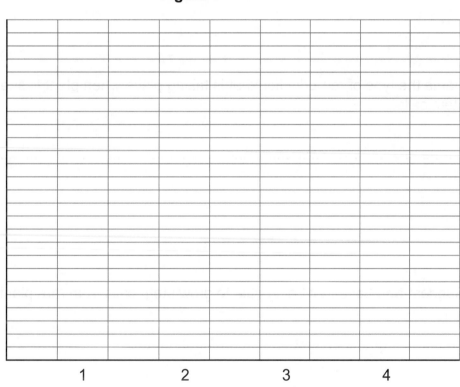

Growth medium

[3 marks]

5.2 Which growth medium produced the best results?

....

[1 mark]

Question 5 continues on the next page

Turn over ▶

5.3   Give **two** variables that needed to be controlled in this experiment.

1. ....

2. ....

[2 marks]

5.4   Suggest how the student could improve their method to reduce the effect of random errors.

....

....

[2 marks]

5.5   Name the type of reproduction that is taking place when plant tissue is grown from stem cells.

....

[1 mark]

5.6   Suggest **one** benefit of being able to grow stem cells from rare plants.

....

[1 mark]

6   **Figure 8** shows a single-celled organism called *Euglena*, found in pond water.

Figure 8

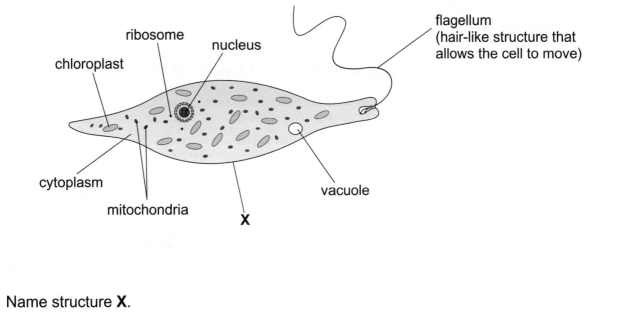

6.1   Name structure **X**.

....

[1 mark]

6.2   *Euglena* is a eukaryote. Which of the following is **not** a eukaryote?
Tick **one** box.

☐   sperm cell   ☐   muscle cell   ☐   fruit fly   ☐   *E. coli* bacteria

[1 mark]

Question 6 continues on the next page

6.3   A scientist viewed an individual *Euglena* under a microscope with × 500 magnification. He calculated the real length of the *Euglena* to be 0.054 mm.

Calculate the length of the image of the *Euglena*. Give your answer in centimetres.

Use the formula:

image size = real size × magnification

....

....

....

image size = ... cm

[2 marks]

6.4   Explain why *Euglena* is able to exchange all of the substances that it needs across its surface.

....

....

[1 mark]

6.5 When *Euglena* was first discovered, scientists disagreed over whether it was a plant or an animal.

Compare the features of plant and animal cells.

Include details of their features in your answer.

....

....

....

....

....

....

....

....

....

....

....

[6 marks]

Turn over for the next question

7   Measles, mumps and rubella are all examples of communicable diseases.

7.1   How is measles spread between people?
Tick **one** box.

☐ By droplets from an infected person's sneeze or cough.

☐ By sexual contact.

☐ By eating contaminated food.

☐ By a vector.

[1 mark]

7.2   The MMR vaccine protects against measles, mumps and rubella.
Explain how vaccination helps to protect the body against a disease.

....

....

....

....

....

....

[4 marks]

7.3   Why might someone **not** want to have the MMR vaccine? Suggest **two** reasons.

1. ....

....

2. ....

....

[2 marks]

Zika virus disease is another example of a communicable disease.
The virus that causes the disease is spread by a mosquito vector.

7.4 Suggest **two** ways that the spread of the Zika virus disease could be reduced.

....Turn over....

....

....

[2 marks]

7.5 Plants are also affected by diseases.

Plants can be infected by a disease called rose black spot.
When a plant has rose black spot, it is important to strip the leaves off the plant.

Explain why it is important to also destroy the stripped leaves.

....

....

[2 marks]

Turn over for the next question

Turn over ▶

8 Different chemical reagents can be used to test for the presence of certain molecules in samples of food.

8.1 A student prepared a food sample in order to test whether the sample contained protein. What reagent should be used for this test?
Tick **one** box.

☐ Benedict's solution

☐ iodine solution

☐ biuret solution

☐ Sudan III stain solution

[1 mark]

8.2 Suggest **one** measure the student should take to make sure the food test is carried out safely.

....
[1 mark]

The student tested four different food samples for reducing sugars.
She obtained the results shown in **Table 3**.

Table 3

Sample	Colour of sample
A	blue
B	brick-red
C	yellow
D	green

8.3 Name the reagent that the student would have used to test for reducing sugars.

....
[1 mark]

8.4 Which of the samples in **Table 3** did **not** contain reducing sugars?
Tick **one** box.

☐ A

☐ B

☐ C

☐ D

[1 mark]

Lactase is an enzyme involved in digestion. Lactase breaks down a sugar called lactose. The products are the sugars glucose and galactose. These are absorbed into the blood from the small intestine.

8.5 Describe how the small intestine is adapted to absorb molecules such as glucose.

....

....

....

....

[3 marks]

8.6 Lactose intolerance is a digestive problem caused by insufficient production of lactase.

To test a person for lactose intolerance, they are given a drink of lactose solution.
A blood sample is then taken from them every 30 minutes for two hours.
The blood is tested to see how much sugar it contains.

If the person has lactose intolerance, their blood sugar level will **not** rise. Explain why.

....

....

[1 mark]

Question 8 continues on the next page

Digestive problems are also seen in people with blocked bile ducts.

8.7   Bile makes conditions in the small intestine alkaline. Give **one** other function of bile.

....

[1 mark]

8.8   Suggest why people with blocked bile ducts have trouble digesting fats.
Refer to your answer to 8.7.

....

....

....

....

[3 marks]

END OF QUESTIONS

CGP Practice Exam Paper GCSE Combined Science

GCSE Combined Science

Biology Paper 2

Foundation Tier

In addition to this paper you should have:
- A ruler.
- A calculator.

Centre name				
Centre number				
Candidate number				

Time allowed:
- 1 hour 15 minutes

Surname	
Other names	
Candidate signature	

Instructions to candidates
- Write your name and other details in the spaces provided above.
- Answer **all** questions in the spaces provided.
- Do all rough work on the paper.
- Cross out any work you do not want to be marked.

Information for candidates
- The marks available are given in brackets at the end of each question.
- There are 70 marks available for this paper.
- You are allowed to use a calculator.
- You should use good English and present your answers in a clear and organised way.
- For Questions 7.4 and 9.5 ensure that your answers have a clear and logical structure, include the right scientific terms, spelt correctly and include detailed, relevant information.

Advice to candidates
- In calculations show clearly how you worked out your answers.

For examiner's use

Q	Attempt Nº			Q	Attempt Nº		
	1	2	3		1	2	3
1				5			
2				6			
3				7			
4				8			
				9			
Total							

1 Hormones control the menstrual cycle.

1.1 How long is a typical menstrual cycle?
Tick **one** box.

☐ 14 days   ☐ 3 months   ☐ 28 days   ☐ 9 months

[1 mark]

1.2 Which hormone causes the release of an egg during the menstrual cycle?
Tick **one** box.

☐ FSH   ☐ LH   ☐ Oestrogen   ☐ Progesterone

[1 mark]

1.3 Some of the hormones involved in the menstrual cycle are released from the pituitary gland. Describe how these hormones reach their target organs in the reproductive system.

....

[1 mark]

1.4 Give another name for the pituitary gland.

....

[1 mark]

1.5 Give **two** differences between a response controlled by hormones and a response controlled by nerves.

1. ....

....

2. ....

....

[2 marks]

2   **Figure 1** shows a food chain.

Figure 1

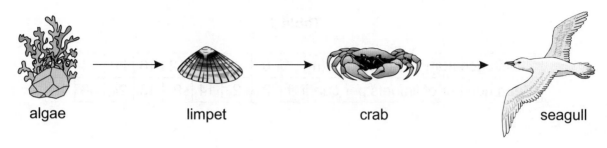

algae   limpet   crab   seagull

2.1   Identify the producer in the food chain in **Figure 1**.
Tick **one** box.

☐ algae   ☐ limpet   ☐ crab   ☐ seagull

[1 mark]

2.2   Name **one** organism in the food chain in **Figure 1** that is prey for another organism.

....
[1 mark]

2.3   Limpets are affected by biotic and abiotic factors in their environment.
Which of the following are abiotic factors?
Tick **two** boxes.

☐ temperature

☐ food availability

☐ moisture level

☐ competition

[2 marks]

Question 2 continues on the next page

Turn over ▶

194

A student investigated the distribution of limpets on a beach. The student used a quadrat to take samples at set distances from the tide's lowest point.
Table 1 shows the results.

Table 1

Distance from low-tide point (m)	0	4	8	12	16	20	24	28
Mean number of limpets per quadrat	3	2	14	9	13	24	38	42

2.4 The student plotted a graph of the results.
Complete **Figure 2** by plotting the final **two** results on the graph.

Figure 2

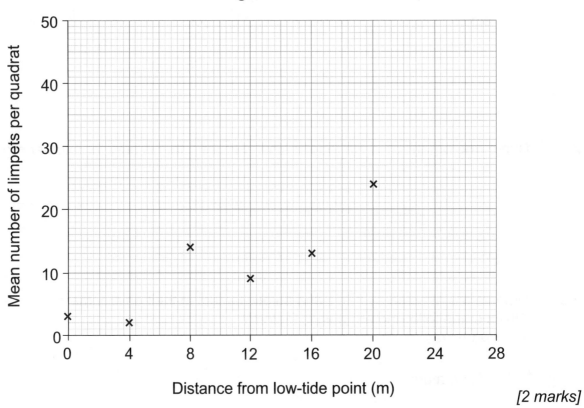

Distance from low-tide point (m)

[2 marks]

2.5 What conclusion can be drawn from the data?
Tick **one** box.

☐ The mean number of limpets is lower at the low-tide point than at 28 m from the low-tide point.

☐ As the distance from the low-tide point increases the number of limpets always increases.

☐ The mean number of limpets increases towards the low-tide point.

☐ The mean number of limpets is constant across the beach.

[1 mark]

2.6 Give **two** possible causes of the variation in limpet distribution.

1. ....

2. ....

[2 marks]

Turn over for the next question

Turn over ▶

3   Fruit flies usually have red eyes.

However, there are a small number of white-eyed fruit flies.

The allele for red eyes (R) is dominant over the allele for white eyes (r).

3.1   What is meant by the term 'allele'?

....

[1 mark]

Figure 3 shows a cross between two heterozygous fruit flies.

Figure 3

	R	r
R		Rr
r		

3.2   Complete **Figure 3**.

[2 marks]

3.3   Give the **two** possible genotypes of fruit flies with red eyes.

....

[1 mark]

3.4 In the genetic cross shown in **Figure 3,** what is the probability of producing offspring with white eyes?
Tick **one** box.

☐ 0.5   ☐ 0.3   ☐ 0.75   ☐ 0.25

[1 mark]

3.5 Fruit flies have the same sex chromosomes as humans.
What combination of sex chromosomes are found in human males?

....
[1 mark]

Turn over for the next question

Turn over ▶

4 Reproduction can be sexual or asexual.

4.1 Sexual reproduction involves gametes.
Use words from the box to complete the sentences about how gametes form.

different	identical	mitosis	four	meiosis	two

During gamete production the parent cell divides by ....

The number of new cells produced is .... Each new cell only

has a single set of chromosomes and is genetically ....

[3 marks]

4.2 Elephants have 56 chromosomes in their body cells.
How many chromosomes will there be in a single elephant gamete?

....
[1 mark]

A population may become extinct if the environment changes quickly and the
population doesn't adapt to the new conditions.

4.3 A population that reproduces asexually might be more likely to become extinct than a
population that reproduces sexually. Suggest why.

....

....

....

....
[3 marks]

5 **Figure 4** shows the yield of tomatoes grown on a farm over a six year period.

Figure 4

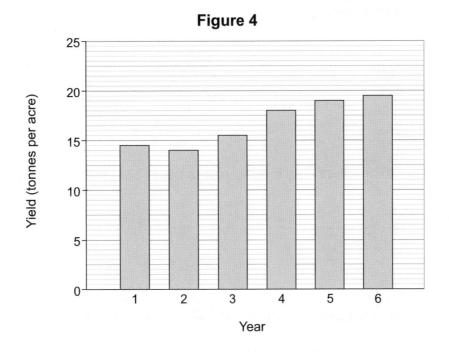

Year

5.1 Explain how selective breeding could have been used to produce the results shown in **Figure 4.**

....

....

....

....

[3 marks]

5.2 A new disease has begun to spread in the tomato plants. Explain why the new disease might pose a large threat to the selectively bred tomato plants.

....

....

....

[2 marks]

Question 5 continues on the next page

Turn over ▶

Some tomato plants have been genetically engineered to be resistant to disease.

5.3   What is genetic engineering?

....

....

[1 mark]

5.4   Give **one** other example of how tomato plants could be genetically engineered.

....

[1 mark]

Some people have concerns about genetically modified crops.

5.5   Genetically modified tomatoes can be grown in enclosed greenhouses, rather than in fields. Suggest how this could reduce concerns about the tomato crop.

....

....

[1 mark]

6   The pancreas plays an important role in controlling the blood glucose level.
Figure 5 shows some of the glands that make up the human endocrine system.

Figure 5

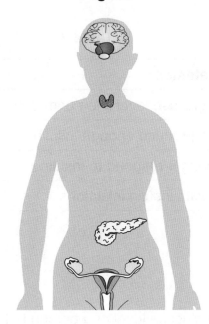

6.1   Label the pancreas on **Figure 5**.

[1 mark]

6.2   When the blood glucose level is too high, the pancreas produces insulin.
Describe how this acts to lower the blood glucose level.

....

....
[1 mark]

Question 6 continues on the next page

Turn over ▶

6.3 People with diabetes have difficulty controlling their blood glucose level.
There are two types of diabetes, type 1 and type 2.

Complete **Table 2** to show whether the statements apply to type 1, type 2 or both.
Put **one** tick in each row.

Table 2

Statement	Type 1	Type 2	Both
Results in a high blood glucose level if left untreated.			
The pancreas fails to produce enough insulin.			
Body cells can no longer respond to insulin.			
Must be treated with insulin injections.			

[4 marks]

Table 3 shows the blood glucose level of a person before and after eating a meal containing carbohydrate.

Table 3

	Before	After
Blood glucose level (mg/dl)	89	146

6.4 Calculate the percentage increase in the person's blood glucose level after the meal.
Give your answer to two significant figures.

....

....

Percentage increase = ... %

[2 marks]

7   A student was investigating the distribution of buttercups in an area around his school.
He counted the number of buttercups in 5 quadrats in five different fields.
His quadrat measured 1 m². His results are shown in **Table 4**.

Table 4

Field	Mean number of buttercups per quadrat
A	10
B	35
C	21
D	37
E	21

7.1   What is the median of the data in **Table 4**?

....

[1 mark]

7.2   A week later, the student repeated his experiment in a sixth field, Field **F**.
His results for each quadrat are shown below:

9   14   19   5   3

Using this data, calculate the mean number of buttercups per m² in Field **F**.

....

....

Mean = ... buttercups per m²

[2 marks]

7.3   Suggest **one** improvement to the student's method.

....

[1 mark]

Question 7 continues on the next page

Turn over ▶

The student observed that the distribution of buttercups changed across Field **A**. Buttercups grow well in damp soil, so the student thinks that the change in the distribution of buttercups is due to variability in the moisture level of the soil across the field. The student wants to investigate this.

7.4 Suggest a hypothesis about the distribution of buttercups in Field **A**, based on the student's observations.

....

....

[1 mark]

7.5 Describe how the student could investigate this hypothesis.

....

....

....

....

....

....

....

....

[4 marks]

8 The peppered moth is an insect that lives on the trunks of trees in Britain.
The moths are prey for birds such as thrushes.

The peppered moth exists in two varieties:

- A light-coloured variety that is better camouflaged on tree trunks in unpolluted areas.
- A dark-coloured variety that is better camouflaged on sooty tree trunks in badly polluted areas.

Figures 6 and **7** show these two varieties of moths on different tree trunks.

| **Figure 6** | **Figure 7** |

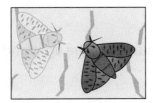 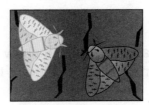

The dark variety of the moth was first recorded in the North of England in 1848.

It became increasingly common in polluted areas until the 1960s, when the number of soot covered trees declined because of the introduction of new laws.

8.1 The binomial name of the peppered moth is *Biston betularia*.
What is the moth's genus?

....

[1 mark]

8.2 Suggest how the dark variety of moth is likely to have first arisen in the population.

....

[1 mark]

Question 8 continues on the next page

Turn over ▶

8.3 Using the idea of natural selection, explain why the dark variety of moth became more common in soot polluted areas.

....

....

....

....

[3 marks]

The bar charts in **Figure 8** show the percentages of the light and dark varieties of peppered moths in two different towns.

Figure 8

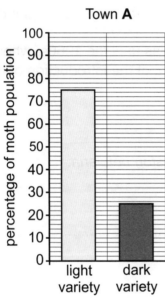 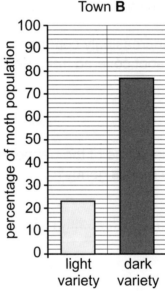

8.4 State which town, **A** or **B**, is the most polluted. Give a reason for your answer.

....

....

[1 mark]

9   A scientist was investigating the reflex actions of males and females.

The scientist made the following hypothesis:

'Males have faster reaction times than females.'

The reaction times of eight participants were tested in the investigation.
Each participant was tapped just below the knee with a small rubber hammer.
When the leg was tapped it automatically kicked outwards at the knee.

The scientist recorded how long it took each participant to respond to
the stimulus of the tap on the leg. Each participant did the test 20 times,
and a mean reaction time was calculated (to 2 decimal places).

The results are shown in **Table 5**.

Table 5

Sex	Participant	Age (years)	Mean reaction time (s)
Female	1	29	0.04
	2	26	0.06
	3	24	0.06
	4	27	0.04
Male	5	19	0.05
	6	22	0.04
	7	25	0.04
	8	20	0.05

9.1   How can you tell that the participants' response was a reflex?
Give **two** reasons.

1. ....

....

2. ....

....
[2 marks]

Question 9 continues on the next page

Turn over ▶

Figure 9 shows the mean reaction times for males and females in the investigation.

Figure 9

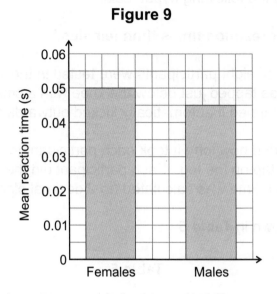

9.2 What can be concluded from the data in **Figure 9**?
Refer back to the scientist's hypothesis in your answer.

....

....

[2 marks]

9.3 Suggest **one** variable that the scientist should have controlled in this experiment.

....

[1 mark]

9.4 Another example of a reflex is the response of moving your hand away from a painful stimulus. The pain stimulus is detected by receptors in the skin and causes a reflex response.

Describe the path taken by a nervous impulse in this reflex, beginning at the receptors.

....

....

....

....

....

....

....

....

....

....

....

[6 marks]

END OF QUESTIONS

Topic 1 — Cell Biology

Page 22
Warm-Up Questions
1) mitochondria
2) Any two from: e.g. plant cells have a rigid cell wall and animals do not. / Plant cells have a permanent vacuole and animals do not. / Plant cells contain chloroplasts and animals do not.
3) False

Bacterial cells have a single loop of DNA instead.

4) electron microscope
5) 4.5×10^{-4} μm

Exam Questions
1 bacterial cell *[1 mark]*
2.1 C *[1 mark]*
2.2 allows photosynthesis to take place *[1 mark]*
2.3 making proteins *[1 mark]*
3.1 How to grade your answer:

Level 0: There is no relevant information. *[No marks]*

Level 1: There is a brief explanation of how to prepare a slide. *[1 to 2 marks]*

Level 2: There is a detailed explanation of how to prepare a slide. *[3 to 4 marks]*

Here are some points your answer may include:
Add a drop of water to the middle of a clean slide.
Cut up an onion and separate it out into layers.
Use tweezers to peel off some epidermal tissue from the bottom of one of the layers.
Use tweezers to place the epidermal tissue into the water on the slide.
Add a drop of iodine solution/stain.
Place a cover slip on top without trapping any air bubbles.
3.2 real size = 7.5 mm ÷ 100 = 0.075 mm *[1 mark]*
$0.075 \times 1000 = \mathbf{75}$ **μm** *[1 mark]*

Page 29
Warm-Up Questions
1) differentiation
2) The cell has a hair-like shape, which gives it a large surface area to absorb water and minerals from the soil.
3) 2
4) in the nucleus
5) True

Exam Questions
1

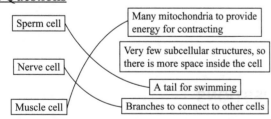

[1 mark for each correct link]

2.1

[1 mark for arrow at shoot tip, 1 mark for arrow at root tip]

2.2 E.g. stem cells can be used to make clones *[1 mark]* of crop plants that have useful features / that aren't killed by a disease *[1 mark]*.
2.3 E.g. paralysis / diabetes *[1 mark]*

Pages 38-39
Warm-Up Questions
1) diffusion
2) True
3) They increase the surface area.
4) E.g. alveoli (in the lung)
5) Stomata
6) E.g. it is made up of lots of thin plates which give a large surface area. / The plates have lots of blood capillaries. / The plates have a thin layer of surface cells.

Exam Questions
1.1

[1 mark for dye particles spread out evenly]

1.2 A higher temperature would increase the rate of diffusion *[1 mark]*.
2.1 The movement of substances from an area of lower concentration to an area of higher concentration, requiring energy. *[1 mark]*
2.2 Movement of mineral ions from the soil into root hair cells *[1 mark]*
Movement of nutrients, such as glucose, from the gut into the blood *[1 mark]*
3.1 partially permeable membrane *[1 mark]*

Remember that osmosis always takes place across a partially permeable membrane.

3.2 The liquid level on side B will fall. *[1 mark]*

This is because water will flow from a less concentrated solution to a more concentrated solution.

4.1

Cylinder	1	2	3	4
Length after 24 hours (mm)	40	43	51	55
Change in length (mm)	**−10**	**−7**	**+1**	**+5**

[1 mark]

4.2 The concentration of the sugar solution that cylinder 4 was placed in must have been lower than the concentration of the solution inside the potato cells *[1 mark]*, so the cylinder increased in length as water entered the cells by osmosis *[1 mark]*.

Topic 2 — Organisation

Pages 48-49
Warm-Up Questions
1) organ
2) active site
3) amylase
4) glycerol and fatty acids
5) False

Proteases are made in the stomach, pancreas and small intestine.

6) E.g. break up the food using a pestle and mortar. Then transfer the ground up food to a beaker and add some distilled water. Next, stir the mixture with a glass rod, and finally filter the solution using a funnel lined with filter paper.

Exam Questions

1.1   A *[1 mark]*

1.2   Bile makes conditions in the small intestine **alkaline** *[1 mark]*. Bile also emulsifies **lipids** *[1 mark]*.

2.1   40 °C *[1 mark]*

2.2   optimum temperature *[1 mark]*

3.1   The enzyme has a specific shape which will only fit with one type of substrate *[1 mark]*.

3.2   It would affect the bonds holding the enzyme together and change the shape of the enzyme's active site/ denature the enzyme *[1 mark]*. This would mean the substrate would no longer fit into it so the enzyme wouldn't work anymore *[1 mark]*.

A similar thing happens when the pH or the temperature is too high — the bonds are disrupted and the shape of the active site may change.

4.1   Biuret solution *[1 mark]*

4.2   Yes, because when iodine solution was added, it turned blue-black *[1 mark]*.

4.3   Yes, because when Sudan III stain solution was added, the mixture separated out into two layers with a red top layer *[1 mark]*.

5.1   To prevent the starch coming into contact with amylase in the syringe, which would have started the reaction before he had started the stop clock *[1 mark]*.

5.2   Rate = $1000 \div 60 = 16.666...$ *[1 mark]*
$$= 17 \text{ s}^{-1} \text{ (2 s.f.)} \text{ [1 mark]}$$

Pages 55-56
Warm-Up Questions

1)   bronchi

2)   They supply oxygenated blood to the heart itself.

3)   Makes the heart beat regularly.

4)   They carry blood back to the heart.

5)   True

Exam Questions

1.1   aorta *[1 mark]*

1.2   It pumps blood around the body. *[1 mark]*

1.3   vena cava *[1 mark]*

2

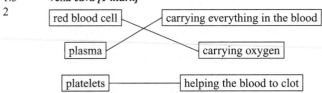

[2 marks for all lines correct, otherwise 1 mark for one line correct.]

3   The shape gives it a large surface area for absorbing oxygen *[1 mark]*.

4.1 $492 \div 12$
= 41 breaths per minute *[1 mark]*

4.2   Resting heart rate is controlled by a group of cells in the right atrium wall that act as a pacemaker *[1 mark]*.

5.1   How to grade your answer:

Level 0:   There is no relevant information. *[No marks]*

Level 1:   There are some relevant points explaining how the structure of a capillary allows it to carry out its function. *[1 to 2 marks]*

Level 2:   There is a clear, detailed explanation of how the structure of a capillary allows it to carry out its function. *[3 to 4 marks]*

Here are some points your answer may include:
Capillaries have gaps in their walls.
This means that substances can diffuse in and out.
Their walls are usually only one cell thick.
This means that diffusion is very fast because there is only a short distance for molecules to travel.

5.2 $1.155 \text{ l} \times 1000 = 1155 \text{ ml}$
$= 1155 \div 2.5 = $ **462 ml/min** *[2 marks for correct answer, otherwise 1 mark for correct working.]*

Make sure you read the question carefully — if you gave your answer in l/min you wouldn't have got all the marks available.

Page 60
Warm-Up Questions

1)   the coronary arteries

2)   An artificial heart could be fitted.

3)   A mechanical device that is put into a person to pump blood if their own heart fails.

Exam Questions

1.1

Description of treatment	Name of treatment
Tubes that are put inside arteries to keep them open	**stents**
Drugs that reduce cholesterol in the blood	**statins**

[1 mark for each correct answer]

1.2   E.g. a person has to remember to take them regularly. / They can cause unwanted side effects. / It takes time for them to work *[1 mark]*.

2.1   biological valves *[1 mark]*, mechanical valves *[1 mark]*

2.2   E.g. it requires surgery, which could lead to bleeding/infection. / There could be problems with blood clots *[1 mark]*.

3.1   fatty material/fatty deposit *[1 mark]*

3.2   The fatty material causes the coronary arteries to become narrow, so blood flow to the heart muscle is reduced *[1 mark]*. This reduces (or stops) the delivery of oxygen to the heart muscle *[1 mark]*.

Page 66
Warm-Up Questions

1)   False

2)   It can be spread from person to person or between animals and people.

3)   True

4)   cancer

Exam Questions

1   A disease that cannot be spread between people or between animals and people *[1 mark]*.

2

	Benign	Malignant
The tumour is made up of a mass of cells formed by uncontrollable division and growth.	✓	✓
The tumour cells can break off and travel into the bloodstream.		✓
The tumour is cancerous.		✓

[1 mark for each correct row]

3.1   A risk factor is something that is linked to an increased chance of getting a certain disease *[1 mark]*.

3.2   e.g. smoking *[1 mark]*

3.3   e.g. ionising radiation *[1 mark]*

Pages 71-72
Warm-Up Questions
1) At the growing tips of shoots and roots.
2) palisade layer
3) False
4) light intensity / temperature / air flow / humidity

Exam Questions
1.1 spongy mesophyll tissue *[1 mark]*
1.2 epidermal tissue *[1 mark]*
2.1 phloem *[1 mark]*
2.2 To allow the cell sap to flow through *[1 mark]*.
2.3 translocation *[1 mark]*
3.1 guard cells *[1 mark]*
3.2 Condition B, because the stoma has closed to reduce water loss *[1 mark]*.
4.1 They are made of dead cells joined end to end *[1 mark]* with no end walls between them and therefore a hole down the middle *[1 mark]*. They're strengthened with a material called lignin *[1 mark]*.
4.2 transpiration *[1 mark]*
5.1 A, because transpiration is faster when the temperature is higher / when the humidity is lower *[1 mark]*.
5.2 How to grade your answer:

Level 0: There is no relevant information. *[No marks]*
Level 1: There are some relevant points explaining how the rate of water loss would be affected by windy weather, but some detail is missing. *[1 to 2 marks]*
Level 2: There is a clear, detailed explanation of how the rate of water loss would be affected by windy weather. *[3 to 4 marks]*

Here are some points your answer may include:
Water is lost more quickly on windy days.
This is because fast-moving air sweeps away the water vapour around the leaf.
This causes the concentration of water vapour inside the leaf to always be higher than outside.
This means water vapour diffuses out quickly.

Topic 3 — Infection and Response

Page 79
Warm-Up Questions
1) True
2) By sexual contact.
3) inside cells
4) A red skin rash.
5) tobacco mosaic virus
6) It causes purple or black spots to develop on the leaves, which can then turn yellow and drop off.

Exam Questions
1 Malaria is caused by a virus *[1 mark]*.
Malaria is caused by a protist, not a virus.
2.1 hand-washing *[1 mark]*
Hand-washing before cooking food can reduce the spread of the disease.
Vaccinations given to chickens (not people) can also reduce the spread.
2.2 vaccinating people *[1 mark]*
3.1 The first symptoms are flu-like *[1 mark]*.
3.2 E.g. pain when the infected person urinates. / Thick yellow or green discharge from the vagina or penis *[1 mark]*.
3.3 E.g. fever / stomach cramps / vomiting / diarrhoea *[1 mark]*

Pages 85-86
Warm-Up Questions
1) The skin stops pathogens getting inside the body and releases substances that kill them.
2) To destroy pathogens that enter the body.
3) Unique molecules on the surface of a pathogen.
4) Through a mutation.
5) Whether the drug works and has the effect you're looking for.

Exam Questions
1.1 Aspirin — Willow
Digitalis — Foxgloves
Penicillin — Mould
[2 marks for three correct lines, otherwise 1 mark for one correct line.]
1.2 painkiller *[1 mark]*
1.3 antibiotic *[1 mark]*
2.1 phagocytosis *[1 mark]*
2.2 Antibodies are produced by **white blood cells** *[1 mark]*. They attach to specific antigens on the surface of the **pathogen** *[1 mark]*.
3.1 human volunteers *[1 mark]*
3.2 Neither the patient or the doctor know who is receiving the drug and who is receiving the placebo *[1 mark]*.
4.1 They trap particles that could contain pathogens *[1 mark]*.
4.2 They move the mucus up to the back of the throat where it can be swallowed *[1 mark]*.
4.3 (hydrochloric) acid *[1 mark]*
5.1 How to grade your answer:

Level 0: There is no relevant information. *[No marks]*
Level 1: There is a brief explanation of how vaccination against rubella can prevent a person catching the disease or how having a large number of vaccinated people in a population reduces the risk of rubella for people who are not vaccinated. *[1 to 2 marks]*
Level 2: There is some explanation of how vaccination against rubella can prevent a person catching the disease and how having a large number of vaccinated people in a population reduces the risk of rubella for people who are not vaccinated. *[3 to 4 marks]*
Level 3: There is a clear and detailed explanation of how vaccination against rubella can prevent a person catching the disease and how having a large number of vaccinated people in a population reduces the risk of rubella for people who are not vaccinated. *[5 to 6 marks]*

Here are some points your answer may include:
When a person is vaccinated against rubella, they are injected with dead or inactive rubella viruses.
The dead or inactive viruses carry antigens, which cause the body to produce antibodies to attack them.
If rubella viruses infect the body after this, white blood cells can quickly produce lots of antibodies to defeat the virus.
If a large number of people in a population are vaccinated against rubella, then there are fewer people who are able to pass the disease on.
This means that even someone who hasn't been vaccinated is less likely to catch the disease.
5.2 E.g. they may be worried that they will have a bad reaction to a vaccine. / Vaccines don't always work and so the person might not be given immunity *[1 mark]*.

Topic 4 — Bioenergetics

Pages 91-92
Warm-Up Questions
1) chlorophyll
2) light

Energy is transferred to chloroplasts from the environment by light.

3) False

Photosynthesis is endothermic.

4) True

Exam Questions
1.1 glucose — $C_6H_{12}O_6$
oxygen — O_2
water — H_2O *[2 marks for 2 correct lines,
1 mark for one correct line.]*
1.2 CO_2 *[1 mark]*
2.1 carbon dioxide + **water** → glucose + **oxygen**
[2 marks — 1 mark for each correct answer.]
2.2 cellulose *[1 mark]*
2.3 storage as oils *[1 mark]*
3.1 it is insoluble *[1 mark]*
3.2 When photosynthesis is not happening, the plant can't produce glucose, so uses stored starch instead *[1 mark]*.
4.1 The rate of photosynthesis is increasing as the concentration of carbon dioxide is increased *[1 mark]*.
4.2 The concentration of carbon dioxide *[1 mark]*.
4.3 The rate of photosynthesis is no longer increasing as the concentration of carbon dioxide is increased *[1 mark]*. The concentration of carbon dioxide is no longer the limiting factor / light intensity or temperature is now the limiting factor *[1 mark]*.

At this point, photosynthesis won't go any faster because another factor is limiting the rate.

4.4 Enzymes needed for photosynthesis will work more slowly at low temperatures *[1 mark]*.
5.1 By counting the number of bubbles produced / by measuring the volume of gas produced in a given time/at regular intervals *[1 mark]*.
5.2 Rate of photosynthesis/number of bubbles in a given time/volume of gas in a given time *[1 mark]*.
5.3 light intensity *[1 mark]*
5.4 E.g. carbon dioxide concentration in the water / temperature / the plant being used *[1 mark]*.

Page 97
Warm-Up Questions
1) True
2) fermentation
3) e.g. increases breathing rate / increases breath volume / increases heart rate
4) urea

Exam Questions
1.1 glucose → lactic acid *[1 mark]*
1.2 Muscles start using anaerobic respiration when they don't get enough **oxygen** *[1 mark]*. This causes a build up of **lactic acid** *[1 mark]*. After anaerobic respiration stops, the body is left with an oxygen **debt** *[1 mark]*.
2 protein *[1 mark]*
3.1 Any two from: e.g. aerobic respiration uses oxygen, anaerobic respiration does not. / Glucose is broken down fully during aerobic respiration but is only partially broken down during anaerobic respiration. / Aerobic respiration doesn't produce lactic acid, anaerobic respiration does. / Aerobic respiration releases more energy than anaerobic respiration. *[2 marks]*

3.2 glucose + **oxygen** → carbon dioxide + **water**
[2 marks — 1 mark for each correct answer.]

Topic 5 — Homeostasis and Response

Page 104
Warm-Up Questions
1) E.g. body temperature / blood glucose level / water content.
2) synapse
3) True
4) E.g. use the same person to catch the ruler each time. / The person should always use the same hand to catch the ruler. / The ruler should always be dropped from the same height.

Exam Questions
1 sensory neurone *[1 mark]*
2.1 appearance of red triangle *[1 mark]*
2.2 cells in the eye / light receptor cells *[1 mark]*
2.3 muscles (in hand controlling mouse) *[1 mark]*
2.4 $343 \times 3 = 1029$
$1029 - 328 - 346 = $ **355 ms** *[2 marks for the correct answer, otherwise 1 mark for the correct working]*

Page 109
Warm-Up Questions
1) In the blood.
2) thyroid
3) False

Type 2 diabetes is where a person becomes resistant to their own insulin.

4) eating a carbohydrate-controlled diet / taking regular exercise

Exam Questions
1

Hormone	Gland the hormone is released from
Testosterone	Testes
Adrenaline	Adrenal gland
Oestrogen	Ovaries

[1 mark for each correct row]

2 Insulin is released by the **pancreas** *[1 mark]*.
Liver and muscle cells convert glucose into **glycogen** *[1 mark]*.

Page 114
Warm-Up Questions
1) testosterone
2) FSH/follicle-stimulating hormone
3) oestrogen and progesterone
4) A chemical that disables or kills sperm.
5) False

Exam Questions
1.1 E.g. facial hair in males / breasts in females *[1 mark]*
1.2 Every 28 days *[1 mark]*
2 diaphragm *[1 mark]*
3.1 It is involved in the growth and maintenance of the uterus lining *[1 mark]*.
3.2 LH / luteinising hormone *[1 mark]*
3.3 They stop the hormone FSH from being released *[1 mark]*, which stops eggs maturing *[1 mark]*.

Topic 6 — Inheritance, Variation and Evolution

Page 121
Warm-Up Questions
1) True
2) two
3) XX

Exam Questions
1 egg — 23 *[1 mark]*
  fertilised egg — 46 *[1 mark]*
2.1 A polymer made up of two strands *[1 mark]*.
2.2 Its genome *[1 mark]*.
Remember, an organism's genome is its entire set of genetic material. A gene is a short section of DNA and a chromosome is a really long structure, which contains genes.
2.3 DNA contains genes *[1 mark]*. Each gene codes for a certain sequence of amino acids *[1 mark]*. The sequence of amino acids are put together to make a specific protein *[1 mark]*.
3.1 asexual *[1 mark]*
3.2 They will be genetically identical *[1 mark]*.
Remember, asexual reproduction produces clones — offspring are exactly the same as the parent.

Page 127
Warm-Up Questions
1) An allele.
2) The characteristics an organism has.
3) It's a genetic disorder where a baby is born with extra fingers or toes.
4) E.g. it will help to stop people suffering. / Treating disorders costs a lot of money.

Exam Questions
1 heterozygous — having two different alleles
  homozygous — having two of the same allele
  genotype — the mix of alleles in an organism
  [2 marks for all lines correct, 1 mark for one correct line.]
2.1

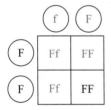

  [1 mark for correct genotype of offspring, 1 mark for correct genotypes of gametes]
2.2 1 in 2 / 50% *[1 mark]*
2.3 One does not have cystic fibrosis and is not a carrier *[1 mark]*. The other does not have cystic fibrosis but is carrier of the condition *[1 mark]*.

Page 134
Warm-Up Questions
1) False
2) False
3) When no individuals of a species are left.
4) A drug that kills bacteria.

Exam Questions
1.1 The appearance of this stingray's ancestors showed **variation** *[1 mark]*. The ancestors that looked like flat rocks were hidden, so were more likely to **survive** *[1 mark]*. They were more likely to reproduce and pass their genes on to the next **generation** *[1 mark]*.
1.2 a mutation *[1 mark]*
2.1 The difference in weight must be caused by the environment *[1 mark]*, because the twins have exactly the same genes *[1 mark]*.
In this case, the environment can mean the amount of food each twin eats or the amount of exercise they each do.
2.2 If they were caused by genes both twins should have the birthmark *[1 mark]*.

Page 138
Warm-Up Questions
1) True
2) GM/genetically modified crops
3) E.g. human insulin

Exam Questions
1 In a population of selectively bred plants, there will be fewer different **alleles** *[1 mark]*. This means if a new disease appears, the plants may be **less resistant** *[1 mark]*. Due to inbreeding, there's also more chance of selectively bred plants having **health problems** *[1 mark]*.
2.1 E.g. to improve the size/quality of their fruit. / To make them resistant to insects/herbicides *[1 mark]*.
2.2 E.g. some people are worried that we might not fully understand the effects of GM crops on human health. / Some people say that growing GM crops will negatively affect the number of wild flowers and insects that live in and around the crops. *[1 mark]*
3.1 Difference between generations 2 and 3 =
  5750 − 5375 = 375
  Percentage change = (375 ÷ 5375) × 100
        = 6.976
        = 7% *[2 marks for the correct answer, otherwise 1 mark for correct working.]*
To work out the percentage change, you first need to work out the difference between generations 2 and 3. You then divide the difference by the original average milk yield (generation 2), and multiply by 100 to convert it into a percentage.
3.2 How to grade your answer:

Level 0:	There is no relevant information. *[No marks]*
Level 1:	There are some relevant points describing how a higher milk yield was produced by selective breeding, but the answer is missing some detail. *[1 to 2 marks]*
Level 2:	There is a clear, detailed explanation of how a higher milk yield was produced by selective breeding. *[3 to 4 marks]*

  Here are some points your answer may include:
  From the existing cows, the farmer selected the cows that produced the highest average milk yield for breeding.
  The farmer then selected the offspring that produced the highest average milk yield for breeding.
  The farmer would have continued this process over several generations of cows.
  After several generations, the farmer would get cows that are able to produce a very high milk yield.

Page 142
Warm-Up Questions
1) True
2) True
3) genus
4) species

Exam Questions
1.1 Prokaryotes *[1 mark]*
1.2 Carl Woese *[1 mark]*
2.1 E.g. from gradual replacement by minerals. / From casts and impressions. / From preservation in places where no decay happens *[1 mark]*.
2.2 Many early organisms were soft-bodied, so their tissue decayed away completely *[1 mark]*. Geological activity may have destroyed some of the fossils that were already formed in rock *[1 mark]*.
2.3 They show how much or how little different organisms have changed over time *[1 mark]*.
3.1 Species C *[1 mark]*
3.2 Yes, you would expect Species D to look similar to Species E because they share a recent common ancestor, so they are closely related/have similar genes *[1 mark]*.

Topic 7 — Ecology

Page 149
Warm-Up Questions
1) e.g. territory/space / mates
2) e.g. moisture level / light intensity / temperature / carbon dioxide level / wind intensity/direction / oxygen level / soil pH/mineral content
3) False
Food chains always start with a producer.
4) it would decrease

Exam Questions
1.1 A habitat is the place where an organism lives *[1 mark]*.
1.2 community *[1 mark]*
2.1 tertiary consumer *[1 mark]*
2.2 The algae are producers *[1 mark]*. They are the source of biomass/energy for the food chain *[1 mark]*.
3.1 A behavioural adaptation *[1 mark]*.
3.2 E.g. it has webbed feet/flippers *[1 mark]* so it can swim for food *[1 mark]*. / It has a thick layer of fat *[1 mark]* to help it keep in heat *[1 mark]*.

Pages 154-155
Warm-Up Questions
1) E.g. a quadrat.
2) e.g. rain / snow / hail
3) To break down/decay dead matter and animal waste.
4) Through burning.

Exam Questions
1 Energy from the sun makes water **evaporate** *[1 mark]*. When warm water vapour gets higher up, the water vapour cools and **condenses** *[1 mark]*. Water falls from the clouds as **precipitation** *[1 mark]*.
2.1 E.g. the number of poppies increases with increasing distance from the wood *[1 mark]*.
2.2 E.g. moisture level / soil pH / soil mineral content

/ wind intensity / wind direction *[1 mark]*.
3.1 eating *[1 mark]*
3.2 respiration *[1 mark]*
3.3 Microorganisms break down/decay the dead matter *[1 mark]* and return carbon to the air as carbon dioxide through respiration *[1 mark]*.
3.4 photosynthesis *[1 mark]*
4.1 Grass species = 47 squares out of 100
= (47 ÷ 100) × 100 = 47% *[1 mark]*
Remember, to calculate percentage cover of an organism in a quadrat you count the number of squares which are more than half covered by the organism.
4.2 E.g. because there may have been too many blades of grass to count each one individually / it's hard to count individual blades of grass *[1 mark]*.

Page 162
Warm-Up Questions
1) Biodiversity is the variety of different species of organisms on Earth, or within an ecosystem.
2) e.g. toxic chemicals for farming / household waste in landfill
3) methane and carbon dioxide
4) True
5) The cutting down of forests.

Exam Questions
1.1 Hedgerows provide a habitat for lots of types of organisms *[1 mark]*.
1.2 The animal species can be bred in captivity *[1 mark]*. This makes sure that some individuals will survive if the species dies out in the wild *[1 mark]*. These individuals can then be released into the wild to replace a population that has been wiped out *[1 mark]*.
2.1 E.g. smoke *[1 mark]*, acidic gases *[1 mark]*.
2.2 E.g. sewage/toxic chemicals from industry can pollute lakes/rivers/oceans. / Fertilisers/other chemicals used on land can be washed into water *[1 mark]*.
2.3 E.g. the human population size is increasing *[1 mark]*, people around the world are demanding a higher standard of living *[1 mark]*.
2.4 This reduces the amount of land taken over for landfill, so ecosystems can be left alone *[1 mark]*.
3 How to grade your answer:
Level 0: There is no relevant information. *[No marks]*
Level 1: There is a brief explanation of how deforestation contributes to global warming. The answer lacks coherency. *[1 to 2 marks]*
Level 2: There is some explanation of how deforestation contributes to global warming, and the answer has some structure. *[3 to 4 marks]*
Level 3: There is a clear and detailed explanation of how deforestation contributes to global warming. *[5 to 6 marks]*
Here are some points your answer may include:
Trees take in carbon dioxide/CO_2 from the atmosphere during photosynthesis.
So cutting down trees means that less carbon dioxide/CO_2 is removed from the atmosphere.
Trees 'lock up' some of the carbon in their wood.
So removing trees means that less is locked up.
Carbon dioxide/CO_2 is released when trees are burnt to clear land.
Microorganisms feeding on dead wood release carbon dioxide/CO_2 through respiration.
Carbon dioxide is a greenhouse gas.
An increase in greenhouse gas levels causes global warming.

Practice Paper 1

1.1   C *[1 mark]*
A is a bronchus, B is the heart and D is an alveolus.
1.2   D *[1 mark]*
1.3   Epithelial tissue — A group of similar cells that work together to carry out a function.
    Respiratory system — A group of organs working together to perform a function.
    Lungs — A group of different tissues that work together to perform a certain function.
    [2 marks for all lines correct, otherwise
    1 mark for one line correct]
1.4   37 *[1 mark]*
When you're calculating a rate, you always divide by time. So here, you need to divide the number of breaths by the number of minutes.
1.5   Gas A — oxygen *[1 mark]*
    Gas B — carbon dioxide *[1 mark]*
2.1   oxygen *[1 mark]*
2.2   chloroplast *[1 mark]*
2.3   making cell walls *[1 mark]*
2.4   damaged *[1 mark]*
2.5   6 *[1 mark]*
2.6   light intensity *[1 mark]*
3.1   Protease — Converts proteins into amino acids.
    Lipase — Converts lipids into fatty acids and glycerol.
    [2 marks for two lines correct, otherwise
    1 mark for one line correct]
3.2   The active sites of different enzymes have different shapes *[1 mark]*. The substance involved in a reaction has to fit into the active site for the enzyme to work *[1 mark]*.
3.3   Enzymes are changed during reactions *[1 mark]*.
3.4   In order to grow, organisms need to transfer energy using respiration *[1 mark]*. Cells need glucose for respiration *[1 mark]*. Amylase provides this glucose by breaking down starch *[1 mark]*.
4.1   The loss of water from a plant *[1 mark]*.
4.2   9 a.m. *[1 mark]*
Each division on the x-axis is one hour.
4.3   E.g. day 2 was colder. / Day 2 was less windy. / Day 2 was wetter/more humid. / The light intensity was lower on day 2 *[1 mark]*.
4.4   Low light intensity at night meant the stomata closed, allowing less water vapour to escape. *[1 mark]*.
4.5   guard cells *[1 mark]*
5.1

Growth medium

[3 marks — 1 mark for a suitable y-axis scale, 2 marks for all bars correct (or 1 mark if two or more bars correct)]

5.2   Growth medium number 1 *[1 mark]*
5.3   Any two from: e.g. the temperature in the incubator / the size of the tissue samples/blocks / the volume of growth medium used *[2 marks — 1 mark for each correct answer]*.
5.4   E.g. grow multiple blocks of stem tissue on each growth medium *[1 mark]* and find the mean for each growth medium *[1 mark]*.
5.5   asexual reproduction *[1 mark]*
5.6   E.g. to prevent the species from going extinct *[1 mark]*.

6.1   cell membrane *[1 mark]*
6.2   *E.coli* bacteria *[1 mark]*
E. coli bacteria are prokaryotes.
6.3   image size = 0.054×500 *[1 mark]*
                 = 27 mm
                 = **2.7 cm** *[1 mark]*
6.4   *Euglena* is a single-celled organism so has a large surface area compared to its volume *[1 mark]*.
6.5   How to grade your answer:
    Level 0: No relevant information is given. *[No marks]*
    Level 1: There is a brief comparison of plant and animal cells, including at least one similarity and one difference. *[1 to 2 marks]*
    Level 2: There is a comparison of plant and animal cells, including at least two similarities and two differences. Some descriptions of subcellular structures are included. *[3 to 4 marks]*
    Level 3: There is a detailed comparison of plant and animal cells, including at least three similarities and three differences. Detailed descriptions of subcellular structures are included. *[5 to 6 marks]*
Here are some points your answer may include:
Similarities:
Both plant and animal cells have a nucleus, which controls the cell's activities.
Both plant and animal cells contain cytoplasm, which is where most of the cell's chemical reactions take place.
Plant cells and animal cells both have a cell membrane, which controls what goes in and out of the cell.
Mitochondria are found in both plant cells and animal cells — these are where most of the reactions for aerobic respiration take place.
Both plant cells and animal cells have ribosomes, which are where proteins are made.
Differences:
Chloroplasts, the site of photosynthesis, are present in plant cells, but not in animal cells.
Plant cells have a cell wall, which supports and strengthens the cell, but animal cells do not.
Plant cells contain a permanent vacuole, containing cell sap, but animal cells do not.
7.1   By droplets from an infected person's sneeze or cough *[1 mark]*.
7.2   How to grade your answer:
    Level 0: There is no relevant information. *[No marks]*
    Level 1: There are some relevant points explaining how vaccination helps to protect the body against disease but the answer is missing some detail. *[1 to 2 marks]*
    Level 2: There is a clear, detailed explanation of how vaccination helps to protect the body against disease. *[3 to 4 marks]*
Here are some points your answer may include:
The body is injected with small amounts of dead or inactive pathogens.
These pathogens have antigens on their surface, which cause the white blood cells in the body to produce antibodies.
Antibodies attack/kill the pathogens.
If live pathogens of the same type appear again, the white blood cells can quickly produce lots of antibodies to kill the pathogens so the person doesn't get ill.
7.3   E.g. vaccines don't always give you immunity. Some people have a bad reaction to a vaccine *[2 marks — 1 mark for each correct answer]*.
7.4   E.g. stop the mosquitoes from breeding. Protect people from mosquito bites using mosquito nets *[2 marks — 1 mark for each correct answer]*.
7.5   To prevent the fungus spreading to other plants *[1 mark]* by being carried by wind or water *[1 mark]*.

8.1   biuret solution *[1 mark]*

8.2   E.g. make sure the area is well ventilated / wear safety goggles / wear gloves / use a funnel when pouring liquids *[1 mark]*.

8.3   Benedict's solution *[1 mark]*

8.4   A *[1 mark]*

Benedict's solution is blue, and so the sample where it stays blue has no reducing sugars.

8.5   It is covered in many villi that provide a large surface area for diffusion (and active transport) to occur across *[1 mark]*. The villi have a thin wall/single layer of surface cells, which decreases the distance for diffusion to occur across *[1 mark]*. They also have a good blood supply to assist quick absorption *[1 mark]*.

8.6   A person with lactose intolerance has little or no lactase to break down the lactose in the drink, so there will be little or no sugar to be absorbed from the small intestine *[1 mark]*.

8.7   Bile emulsifies/breaks down fats *[1 mark]*.

8.8   Fat in the small intestine would not be emulsified/broken down into small droplets *[1 mark]*. This would mean that there is a low surface area for lipase to work on *[1 mark]*, meaning a slow rate of fat digestion *[1 mark]*.

Practice Paper 2

1.1   28 days *[1 mark]*

1.2   LH *[1 mark]*

1.3   The hormones are carried in the blood to their target organs *[1 mark]*.

1.4   master gland *[1 mark]*

1.5   Any two from: nerve-controlled responses are fast-acting while hormone-controlled responses have a slower action. / Nerve-controlled responses act for a short time while hormone-controlled responses act for long time. / Nerve-controlled responses act on a precise area while hormone-controlled responses act more generally.
[2 marks — 1 mark for each correct answer]

2.1   algae *[1 mark]*

2.2   limpet / crab *[1 mark]*

2.3   temperature *[1 mark]*, moisture level *[1 mark]*

2.4

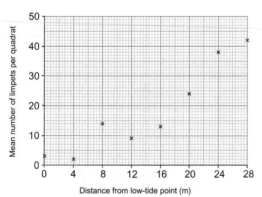

[1 mark for each point plotted correctly]

2.5   The mean number of limpets is lower at the low-tide point than at 28 m from the low-tide point *[1 mark]*.

2.6   Any two from: e.g. variation in competition/predation/food availability/moisture level/temperature/oxygen level
[2 marks — 1 mark for each correct answer]

3.1   A form/version of a gene *[1 mark]*.

3.2

	R	r
R	RR	Rr
r	Rr	rr

[2 marks for all genotypes correct, otherwise 1 mark for one or two correct.]

3.3   RR and Rr *[1 mark]*

3.4   0.25 *[1 mark]*

3.5   XY *[1 mark]*

4.1   meiosis *[1 mark]*, four *[1 mark]*, different *[1 mark]*

4.2   28 *[1 mark]*

4.3   Asexual reproduction happens by mitosis *[1 mark]*. This means there's no genetic variation in the offspring *[1 mark]*. The offspring may not have characteristics that are suited to the new conditions and so the population can't adapt to the new conditions *[1 mark]*.

5.1   The highest yielding tomato plants from the first year could have been selected *[1 mark]* and been bred together *[1 mark]*. This could have been repeated every year *[1 mark]*.

5.2   The number of different alleles/genetic variation in the selectively bred tomato population might be low *[1 mark]*. This would mean it's less likely that the tomato plants will have (alleles for) disease resistance *[1 mark]*.

5.3   A process in which genes from one organism are introduced into the genome of another organism *[1 mark]*.

5.4   E.g. to be resistant to herbicides / to be resistant to insects / to produce bigger fruit / to produce more fruit *[1 mark]*.

5.5   The genetically engineered tomatoes are less likely to affect wild plant populations *[1 mark]*.

6.1

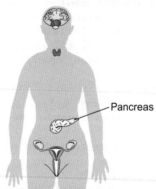

Pancreas

[1 mark]

6.2   Insulin causes glucose to move out of the blood and into cells *[1 mark]*.

6.3

Statement	Type 1	Type 2	Both
Results in a high blood glucose level if left untreated.			✓
The pancreas fails to produce enough insulin.	✓		
Body cells can no longer respond to insulin.		✓	
Must be treated with insulin injections.	✓		

[4 marks — 1 mark for each tick]

6.4   percentage increase = $((146 − 89) ÷ 89) × 100$
        = **64% (2s.f.)** *[2 marks for correct answer, otherwise 1 mark for correct working.]*

7.1   21 *[1 mark]*

To find the median, you write out all the results from lowest to highest, i.e. 10, 21, 21, 35, 37. 21 is in the middle of the list, so it is the median.

7.2 $(9 + 14 + 19 + 5 + 3) ÷ 10$
        $= 50 ÷ 5$
        = **10 buttercups per m²** *[2 marks for correct answer, otherwise 1 mark for correct working.]*

7.3   E.g. use more quadrats in each field *[1 mark]*.

7.4   E.g. more buttercups grow where there is a higher moisture level in the soil *[1 mark]*.

7.5   How to grade your answer:

Level 0:   There is no relevant information. *[No marks]*

Level 1:   There is a brief description of how the student could investigate whether the change in distribution of buttercups is due to variability in the moisture level of the soil. *[1 to 2 marks]*

Level 2:   There is a detailed description of how the student could investigate whether the change in distribution of buttercups is due to variability in the moisture level of the soil. *[3 to 4 marks]*

Here are some points your answer may include:

He could use a transect across Field A.

To do this he should mark out a line across the field.

Then he should record the number of buttercups in quadrats placed next to each other/at intervals along the line.

He should also measure the moisture level of the soil at each sampling point (e.g. with a probe).

8.1   *Biston [1 mark]*

8.2   As a result of mutation(s) *[1 mark]*.

8.3   The dark variety is less likely to be eaten by predators in soot polluted areas (because they are better camouflaged) *[1 mark]* so they are more likely to survive to reproduce *[1 mark]*, meaning that the genes for dark colouring are more likely to be passed on to the next generation and become more common in the population *[1 mark]*.

8.4   Town B is the most polluted because it contains a higher percentage of dark moths *[1 mark]*.

9.1   Their reaction time was very fast *[1 mark]*.

Their response was involuntary/automatic *[1 mark]*.

If you have to think about what response to give then it's not a reflex action.

9.2   The males in this experiment had a faster mean reaction time than the females *[1 mark]*, so the data supports the scientist's hypothesis *[1 mark]*.

9.3   E.g. the age of the participants. / The strength of the tap on the knee. / Caffeine consumption of the participants prior to the investigation. *[1 mark]*

9.4   How to grade your answer:

Level 0:   There is no relevant information. *[No marks]*

Level 1:   There is a brief description of some parts of the path taken by a nervous impulse in the reflex. *[1 to 2 marks]*

Level 2:   There is some description of the path taken by a nervous impulse in the reflex, but some detail is missing. *[3 to 4 marks]*

Level 3:   There is a clear and detailed description of the path taken by a nervous impulse in the reflex. *[5 to 6 marks]*

Here are some points your answer may include:

The impulse travels along a sensory neurone to the central nervous system/spinal cord.

When the impulse reaches a synapse between the sensory neurone and a relay neurone, it triggers chemicals to be released.

These chemicals cause impulses to be sent along the relay neurone.

When the impulse reaches a synapse between the relay neurone and a motor neurone, chemicals are released again which cause impulses to be sent along the motor neurone.

The impulse then reaches the muscle, which contracts to move your hand away from the source of pain.

Index

Index